To Chris and Ann,
1 really hop ... ...-
let me ...

ADAM

By

Michael J Lansdown

The story of one village's quest to uncover its past and understand the divide that is tearing it in two.

Published by
The Endless Bookcase Ltd.
71 Castle Road, St Albans, Hertfordshire,
England, UK, AL1 5DQ.
www.theendlessbookcase.com

Printed Edition
Also available in multiple e-book formats via The Endless Bookcase website, Amazon, Nook and Kobo.

Printed in the United Kingdom
First printing, 2017.

ISBN: 978-1-908941-71-8

Acknowledgements

Thanks go to friends and former colleagues for their encouragement and interest when I was writing this book- especially to Ciaran, Eleri and Mary for your feedback and comments on the earlier drafts, and to David and Hilary for feedback which led to this second edition. Also to my family: Caroline, Bryn and Catrin for your great patience and for keeping my feet on the ground!

Finally, to Carl and Morgana at *The Endless Bookcase* for making the finished book possible.

Dedication

To the memory of my mother and father: you taught me to love words.

About the Author

On gaining a degree and PGCE at the University of Wales, Aberystwyth, Michael spent nearly forty years teaching learners from three years old to those in their eighties. He taught both in the UK and in Sweden where he spent some time teaching adults and children in schools, colleges, evening classes, and industry. He has always had an interest in language and for many years dabbled in song-writing, verse, and other types of factual accounts. This included hyperbolic match reports for Haringey Rugby Club of which he says he is still justly proud.

He always believed himself to have little or no imagination so when, one morning between junctions 18 and 19 of the M25, the idea for *Adam's Lock* came to him he was surprised and encouraged to take it further. Much research into local history and into the eighteenth century penal system followed, eventually leading to the beginnings of a tale he felt he needed to tell.

Two more books are planned to complete the *Adam's Lock* trilogy. Work has already begun on a follow-up which opens in a New South Wales penal colony and ends several years, and many thousands of miles, later on the other side of the world. The third book is planned to take place in the dark years which led up to and culminated in the tragedy of the First World War.

In what is something of a contrast Michael is also writing a humorous account of a primary headteacher taking up his first appointment. Based largely on his own experiences in education it is a blend of fact and imagination taking the reader on a 'Year in the life of...' journey with all its twists and turns.

Like many writers Michael believes that he did not 'decide to become an author'; rather, that he was taken over by a process from which there was no escape. Nevertheless, he feels that if he *had* been given a choice, this is what he would have chosen to do!

Prologue

September 16th 2010
The Field - Hensford High School

The school field.

Children group together- talking and laughing- face to familiar face.

At the first whistle they stop. Some boys dare to move.

At the second whistle they walk, some run, towards the distant doors.

Two boys break from the crowd and, like magnets, are drawn together.

Opposites attract.

Their shoulders touch, their heads turn, and a look darts between their eyes.

'Anytime!' it screams, 'Anytime!': a challenge, as old as time itself.

And then, they are down.

Wild fists, flailing blindly.

Grunting.

Cursing.

Until stronger hands pull them apart.

Chapter One

Saturday July 31st 2010
Alex Clarke's House - Upper Hensford

'Alex! Get a move on; we're going to be late!'

Marjorie Clarke checked her wrist-watch for the third time and tidied her hair in the mirror by the door. It was *always* like this with Alex-on schooldays, or Saturdays, like today, and it really wasn't fair. It wasn't *her* cricket match; she had better things to do than stand in a field all day watching boys trying to hit a ball with a stupid piece of wood.

'Alex! If you're not down in two minutes I'm going back to bed.' She sat heavily on the wicker chair and fiddled with the cuff of her jacket, checking the time again before standing and walking to the bottom of the stairs. 'Alex!'

The sound of heavy footsteps, quickly descending, announced the arrival of her son: cricket-whites and bag. Without stopping, he crossed the lobby floor and threw open the front door before making his way, laces flapping, to the car.

'And a good morning to you too, Alexander,' she said to herself before following her son to where he was waiting, elbow on the roof of the car.

'What?'

'What what? It's twenty to. You're late. We're late. Get in.'

'Open the door then.'

'Done!'

The car threw up gravel as it left the drive and made its way onto the lane leading from the house to the cricket club where play was due to begin in twenty minutes' time. Not much was said as the car negotiated the narrow road- the mother focusing on avoiding the potholes and uncut hedges, the son looking out at the familiar view. It was a warm July morning and Alex pressed the button, allowing a little air into the car.

'Not too much Alex, it's my hair- put it up a bit- use the air con.' Marjorie struggled to keep her focus, split as it was between hair, watch and hedges. Alex reversed the movement of the window a touch, closing it a fraction before resuming his silent observation of the world as it flashed past. What he saw was countryside, but not as his grandfather knew it. The farms were farms in name only and these days you were more likely to fall into a hot-tub than a cattle trough. These sprawling residences, complete with long-redundant chimneys, red-brick and tall, were now the comfortable retreats of the comfortably well-off. Executives and city bankers now lounged in the very rooms formerly occupied by farmers and their families- muck and sweat usurped by the stench of wealth and the unpleasant waft of stale *'Dior pour Homme'*. And between the buildings he caught the odd glimpse of the village far below-the glint of the canal, the tiled roofs of the old industrial area, and the grey walls of the housing estates clinging to the valley bottom.

'Not speaking today?'

Alex shrugged. 'What d'you want me to say?'

'Ooh, I don't know. Good morning? Something about the weather? Something about the game, maybe? Just something.'

'Good morning. It's nice today. I hope we win.'

'Well, that's a start I suppose. Can't you just make an effort to communicate, Alex? I know it's hard when you're nearly thirteen but it doesn't cost anything.' The mother pulled down the visor as the road momentarily disappeared from view.

'Okay. Whatever, mum. Just got a bit of a headache.'

'So, what about the game? *The* game. Are you excited to be playing? Quite an honour to play for The Uppers you know.'

'Look. We always win. The Lowers haven't won the cup since, well, before I was born, and I don't even know which year it was. They're hopeless- haven't got a clue. They play football, and they beat us every year. Hasn't anyone worked that out yet?'

'True, but you have to remember you're representing *our* part of the village-it's a historical thing. At least that's what your father says, and he's been here all his life.'

Alex yawned and ran his hands through his hair before reluctantly tying the laces of his cricket boots. They were almost there and he knew that Dr. Chistie, coach Christie, would not appreciate him turning up looking sloppy. The car made the final turn into the carpark of the clubhouse stopping below the sign that told the world that this was Hensford Cricket Club, established 1889, and that new members were always welcome. The sign itself, in faded green and cream, hung crookedly from rusty hinges and Marjorie, after reconsidering, reversed slowly to a safer parking spot.

'Have you quite finished mum?' Alex asked, before opening the door and stepping out onto the rutted tarmac.

'Yo! Alex!' A gangly boy with the first blush of a beard came out to greet Alex, high-fived him and Marjorie watched as both disappeared to the far side of the old pavilion. Seeing her son walk off, she said 'good luck' to the air and angled the mirror towards herself, then patted her hair and puckered her lips before smoothing down her skirt and getting out of the car. She looked around to see if there was anyone she knew. Nobody she recognised. Normally, it would be Derek doing the cricket duty but he was away- somewhere in Eastern Europe she thought- so this weekend, she had the honour. She decided she would have to be courageous and come from behind the car, but she felt uncomfortable in places with which she was unfamiliar and this, she felt, was just one of those locations. Also, there seemed to be a number of adults from the other side of the valley already congregating, with their grey tracksuit bottoms and baseball caps. She moved cautiously holding her bag close to her body.

'Marge! Coo-ee, over here!'

Thank God, she thought, and turned to see her friend Dee walking -no, marching: Dee always marched- towards her. 'How larvly to see you!' Dee drawled then gave her an air kiss, *mwah, mwah,* one on each cheek.

'Dee, lovely to see *you* too-it must be, oh what, two days now?'

'Oh stop it, Marge. Let's go and get a drink. I think it's going to be a long morning.'

'Dee, it's a quarter past *nine* and normally, if my memory serves me well, the Lowers are all out —is that the right expression?- in about fifteen minutes.'

'Fair point, so let's get in there quick Marge. Just a small drink for goodness sake!' said Dee, and took Marjorie by the elbow, half frog-marching her towards the bar.

Marjorie noticed more parents arriving from the valley bottom and made an effort not to stare. They arrived in their ones and twos, kids stuffed in the backs of ageing estate cars, not a single one, she noted, dressed in the correct attire.

'C'mon Marge. Stop your staring. What's your poison?'

'G&T, with plenty of G please, dear,' she replied, before taking one last peep over her shoulder and disappearing into the gloom of the bar.

*

Alex held his left hand to his eyes, shielding them from the sun that streamed down the wicket.

'Middle and leg, please Sir,' he shouted to the portly man dressed as if he was ready for a day in a school science lab which was (but not at the weekend) precisely where he would normally be.

'That's it- you're there Alex,' came the reply and the boy made his mark on the hard ground of the crease. He looked around at the field to see groups of tracksuited youngsters clearly not paying full attention to the events about to commence at the centre.

'Over or around the wicket?' the umpire asked of the young lad standing ready to bowl. The boy looked confused.

'Which side of the wicket are you going to bowl on-this side, or that side?' he explained further.

'Oh, that side,' he said, pointing to his left.

'Opening over. Right-hand bowler. Coming over the wicket. Play!'

The bowler looked unsure and waited.

'Right Lee, you can start,' said the umpire and fiddled with the pebbles he kept in his pocket. 'Off you go!'

Lee ran to the crease, stopped, then lobbed the ball toward the end where Alex waited. The batsman stepped away from the crease and on its second bounce, with an easy hook, sent the ball high over the boundary and into the long grass. The umpire turned to face the scorers and raised both arms above his head to signal a six. A group of mums and dads cheered, a moan went up from another section of the crowd, Alex raised his bat, and Lee looked at his feet.

'Don't worry lad. Just keep trying. It's early days yet,' said the umpire, then indicated that the batsman was ready for the second delivery. He found another pebble, round and smooth, and fiddled with it between his thumb and forefinger.

Lee replicated his first ball and was forced to duck as the ball narrowly missed his head before skimming its way towards the far boundary. Alex made to run and then motioned to his fellow batsman that he could stay, the ball having evaded the lunging leg of an outfielder to go for four more runs.

Another ironic cheer came from the Uppers answered immediately by the parents and siblings of the fielding team exhorting them to 'catch the bloody thing' and 'remember who you are playing.' At this, Lee looked even more disconsolate and turned to where the comments were loudest, holding his arms out wide as if to say it wasn't his fault, which was, unfortunately for him, only partly true.

The third ball went for a wide and the noise of the spectators began to crowd in on the bowler's head. Determined to redeem himself he lengthened his run-up for the forth delivery and rocketed the ball as hard as he could towards the other end of the wicket. Now it was the batsman's turn to duck, the ball flying close to his head, eventually to be stopped by a surprised-looking fielder before it too reached the boundary.

'Sir! That was a *throw*! Nearly took my head off!' Alex was clearly shocked and waved his bat in anger. The crowd booed, and some cheered, more at the spectacle than through any interest or understanding of what had just occurred.

The umpire turned to Lee and took him aside, shielding him from the view of the majority of spectators clustered around the clubhouse.

'Got to keep your arm straight, Lee. Like this. Not like this. That's a throw, not a bowl and it's not allowed. Understand?'

'Yes ref,' Lee nodded and picked up the ball which had, by a small miracle, rolled up to his feet, then he returned to where his run-up had started a minute earlier. He felt embarrassed, but at the same time, somehow elated. He'd made his mark, and had wiped the grin off Alex Parker's face which for him was a lot more satisfying than taking any wicket.

'*Your* boy's doing well Marge, just scored another boundary.'

'Is he Dee?' said Marjorie, turning to face the action. 'Come on Alexander! Show them what for!' she shouted a little too enthusiastically for a number of the opposing parents who looked across, irritated, but resisting the temptation to shout something they might regret.

'C'mon you Lowers! It's early days!' yelled one of the dads to which a small group nearby added their own cheers and encouragement.

'See what you *did* Marge!' said Dee, privately relishing the needle but at the same time wanting to keep her own head below the parapet. 'Best not have another gin,' she whispered, causing them to dissolve into the fit of giggles for which the two of them were renowned.

'Hate this game, Dee,' Marjorie admitted, revealing nothing new to her best friend. 'But Alex seems to like it and we've drummed it into him what a privilege it is to represent the Uppers. What about you?'

'As you well know, I feel the same, darling. I can't *stand* the standing…' They both giggled into their drinks again before Dee resumed, 'No, no, Marge, seriously I can't stand all the waiting. Most of the time they're not doing anything, or not much at least, and then they're all out until they're in and wait until it's their turn to be in when they all go out. Or something. There's a joke about that isn't there?'

'Wouldn't know Dee, dear.' Another giggle. 'But I do know what you mean. Better than standing on the rugger field though. *Oh my God!* the hours I used to spend watching Derek run up and down the bloody rugger pitch, him huffing and puffing like an old man and me pretending I had the first idea what was going on! And then he'd get injured and expect me to take pity on him, make him cups of tea and things at home. At least it's nice and sunny today and we're unlikely to end up in A&E.'

'Unless you keep on upsetting the locals,' Dee mumbled into her chest, sending them again into a fit of giggles and attracting the attention of a group of supporters from the other side of the village.

'What they f'n laughin' at? Poxy game. Wait till the winter comes and we gets to play football. Then we'll see whose laughin'!' A young mother glared across whilst her friend, Tash, placed her hand on her arm preventing her from flicking the v-sign which she was about to send to Marjorie and Dee, still talking and laughing, unawares.

'Not worth it Bex; like you said, wait till we take them on in football. Just enjoy the sunshine while you can. Fancy another?'

Bex shrugged her shoulders. 'Yeah, why not?'

'Cos you'll get *pissed*, that's why not!' said the man next to her, holding up and tapping the can of special brew he was about to crack open. 'But as you're only young once, go for it,' he laughed. He turned his attention to the pitch where Alex had just been caught out, a wild swing ending his innings with the ball falling into the hands of a tall youngster now being feted by the rest of the excited fielders. 'Come on you Lowers!' he screamed hoisting his can aloft in celebration of this small, unexpected victory.

'So, as I was saying. The one with the multi-coloured hair, she's Becky Hill-Bex to her friends. In and out of trouble with the law and a complete nightmare when her sprogs, twins, were at The Valley. Ended up being banned for a month by the head so she behaves better now with child number three- a girl I believe. Geoff is always reading me things about her from the Law Reports in The Observer - no TV licence, doing fifty down the high street, shouting at neighbours, that sort of thing. She was given an ASBO once too...'

'Oh, we used to have one of those once, but the wheels fell off,' Marjorie interrupted, causing Dee to get tonic water up her nose.

'Oh, stop it, you!' she said. 'Be *serious* for once. She's a nasty piece of work so don't get involved. Let's just saunter casually to the far side of the field-by the big white thing-the screen I think they call it.'

The two women picked up their drinks, linked arms and made their way over to the other side of the field, all the time resisting the temptation to look back. Passing a number of others from the same side of the village, they stopped to chat before eventually settling on a low mound a few yards from the boundary.

Their departure had not gone unnoticed by Bex, Tash and the others, but was soon forgotten as the action on the field took a brief unexpected turn in favour of the Lowers. A number of rash decisions by the lower–order batsmen had resulted in the Uppers being all-out for seventy-three runs, considerably fewer than in previous years. This change in fortunes was greeted by whoops and cheers from the Lowers' supporters, and grudging, muted handclaps from those backing Alex, James and friends.

Following a five-minute pause in which the boys were treated to some juice and biscuits, the first pair of Lowers batsmen waddled their way to the wicket. Mr Taylor, the umpire, checked that the opening batsman was ready and dropped his arm, signalling the start of the over. The boy with the beard, as Marjorie thought of him, toyed with the ball, tossing it from hand to hand before starting his short, slow approach to the crease. The ball left the back of his hand forming a high parabolic loop before pitching close to where the batsman stood, rooted to the spot. In a fraction of a second his time at the stumps was over, the bails falling lazily to the ground, accompanied by an uncomprehending look on his face.

'Owzat!' Several voices appealed as one, and fielders close-by ran to congratulate the bowler when the inevitable finger was raised.

'Bad luck Tyler, out to a great delivery,' said Mr Taylor, as the boy finally came to understand what had transpired and started the long walk back to the pavilion.

Next out was Lee, and as they crossed he grabbed at the bat of the returning batsman, determined not to go out the same way. He had watched some of the Uppers and how they did things, and listened also to the teacher who had volunteered to be their team coach for the day. 'Don't snatch at the ball Lee. Take things a bit more slowly-especially with Thomas when he bowls. You can't hit *everything* over the trees, so just take your time! Good luck,' he'd said, before Lee had taken a deep breath and made his way onto the field.

'Middle and leg, sir,' he said, parroting Alex Parker's instructions an hour earlier. He surveyed the field, as he'd seen Alex do, then nodded his readiness to the umpire. The umpire told him that the bowler was a right-hander and that he was bowling over the wicket. Thomas started his second, slow run-up of the day, sending the ball in the same looping curve, arcing high against the intense blue of the sky. Lee struggled to focus then swiped out as hard as he could, willing the ball over the distant trees. A small, sharp click told him that the ball had by-passed his bat and had nicked the outside of the off stump, causing the bail to duly leave the comfort of its moorings, which in turn prompted the second appeal of the innings. Same appeal. Same finger. The second duck of the morning.

*

For the Lowers, the day hardly improved. Successive batsmen padded up and walked to the centre only to return having barely broken sweat. With the last man ready to do his bit the scoreboard showed only 13 runs, and the hands of the old clock had moved on barely twenty minutes since the last of the biscuits. Two minutes later it was all over, a simple delivery taking out middle stump, much to the amusement of the Uppers contingent.

A loud quacking sound, emanating from the same area, was what set it all off. First, the boy at whom it was directed, burst into tears and flung the bat across the pitch, narrowly missing a startled fielder. Then a bearded man, presumably the batsman's father, exploded from a group of Lowers supporters, shouting a string of obscenities, directed towards the Uppers in general and the originator of the sound in particular. The fielding team grouped at the centre then made their way cautiously together towards their waiting parents, while Mr Taylor and a small number of club officials called for calm and ushered the two sides towards what they hoped were the correct parts of the carpark. Bex and her friends, by now far too gone to know or care about the scoreboard, joined in enthusiastically, goading the Uppers about what would happen in the autumn football match and making worrying comments about needing to *keep an eye in the f'n mirror* as they drove home. Eventually, and much to the relief of Mr Taylor and his colleagues, the last of the vans and ageing estates had left the carpark, the sound of the horns and expletives fading gradually as they dropped into the valley below.

'*Well*!' said Marge when silence had finally descended on the ground again. 'Would you have credited it, Dee?'

The boys, by this time, had found their parents and were sitting, shocked, in small huddles near the clubhouse. The odd one smiled weakly, putting on a brave face, but most simply stared ahead, stunned by the antics of the previous ten minutes. Some looked close to tears.

Dr. Christie was speaking to them, congratulating them on another win, assuring them that none of what had happened was their fault and that they were not to be afraid. A number of parents added a *hear-hear* before leading their boys back to their waiting four-by-fours.

'Well, Marge, time to be heading back I suppose. Lovely to see you again- just a bit shocked really now,' said Dee, the bonhomie of earlier having dissipated like the fizz of her tonic water.

Marge puckered her lips and bent to kiss her friend on the cheek, adding a squeeze of the shoulders for reassurance.

'Same. Chin up and don't let the wotsits get you down. Come on Alex, Star of the Show, time for us to be heading home too. Cold meat and salad for lunch.'

In a little while the place was quiet again. Albert, the groundsman, had retrieved the bat from silly point and put it back in the locker room, checking everything was secure in the clubhouse. The plastic bags full of empty beer-cans could wait till Tuesday when the bin-men came- he'd be glad to be rid of them and all their associations. One last look, then he mounted his old bike, locked the gate behind him, and rode away slowly; home to an early lunch.

Chapter Two

Saturday September 18th 2010
Lee Parker's House - Lower Hensford

'You deal with him. He's your son too you know!' Lesley Parker stuffed her purse into her handbag and took a last mouthful of tea from her mug.

'Give him a break, Les, he's not thirteen yet and he takes all this stuff to heart. I've told him to deal with it, or ignore them, but he won't let it lie- he's a chip off the old block.'

'Yeah, Wayne, like I said- he's your son too, so you can sort him out. I've got to get to work and I'm already in the boss's bad books. Take him fishing or something. Have a talk with him. Like you do- you know, man to man'

Lesley Parker grabbed her mobile and made for the door. She turned, said 'See ya later,' then hurried out.

Wayne Parker stretched his arms above his head, blew out his cheeks then headed for the bottom of the stairs.

'Lee? You up there?' he shouted - no answer. 'Lee! Are you there?' Still no answer. He sighed, then pulled his way to the top, stopping outside the door that said *Lee's Room. Enter at your peril!* He knocked at the door and pushed it open, not waiting for a reply.

The boy on the bed was wearing his headphones, all external sounds blocked out by the music coming from an i-pod.

'What? Dad! Knock before you come in, will you!' He whipped off the phones and threw them onto the floor. 'God, dad, can't I get any peace and quiet around here!'

Wayne Parker held up his hands in surrender. 'I did knock Lee, but with those things on I'd need to blow the bloody door off to get you to hear. Anyhow, I need to talk to you.'

'About what? I don't need to talk.' He paused. 'It's mum, isn't it? She's been havin' a go again.'

The father looked awkward, an exaggerated, pained expression contorting his face.

'It's just we're a bit worried about you, son. Don't seem yourself lately. Bit too quiet, if you know what I mean.'

Lee looked directly at his father. 'Have the school rung or something?'

Wayne stuck out his bottom lip and shrugged. 'Umm, don't think so. Not as I know anyway. Should they have? Something happened?'

The boy sat up on the bed, swung his legs over the side, then slumped down and looked up at his father, his dark fringe getting in the way a bit. 'Had a bit of a fight on the field yesterday afternoon. Coming in from lunchtime. Had to see the head of year.'

'*Thought* you had a bit of a mark by your eye.' Wayne tipped the boy's chin upwards. 'Thought it was from football or something, but now I can see it for what it is, the start of a shiner. What happened? Who started it?'

'Don't know,' Lee lied, merely putting off the inevitable.

'Don't know?' said his father. 'What, it was a sort of alien encounter? Just sort of came out of the blue: zap! *you're dead Parker*!'

The boy groaned. 'Okay, okay I'll tell you. It was the Clarke boy. Alex. He's in my class.'

Now it was the father's turn to groan.

'I bloody knew it! I said to your mum yesterday, I bet the bloody Clarkes have got something to do with this, but she wouldn't have any of it. Go on- tell me more.'

'No, it wasn't anything like *that*,' he said. 'We were just coming in when we sort of bumped into each other.'

'*Just sort of bumped into each other?* As you do?'

'Yeah, there's hundreds of kids all making for the door, and we just sort of crashed into each other...'

'So now, it's *crashed*?'

'Yeah, then I pushed him and he pushed me back and it all sort of kicked off from there and we landed on the ground until a teacher split us up and we had to go in-and that was it.'

'Until you had to go and see the head-teacher or something!'

'*Not* the head-teacher. The head of year.'

'Whatever,' said his father and sat on the bed next to him.

'So, did *he* get into trouble, this Clarke boy?'

'We both got into trouble, dad.'

'Yeah, but he started it. He barged into *you*.'

'We bashed into each other. It was both our faults. Don't start trying to make out that it's always the uppers that start things. It happens all the time- sometimes them, sometimes us.' He held his head in his hands and let out another groan. 'It just pisses me off dad.'

'Language, son. Right, what can we do to make things better?' Wayne looked for a quick solution, a way to bring the conversation to a rapid conclusion. 'Your mother said we should go fishing up the canal. What d'you say- our spot by the lock? Then fish and chips. Just you and me.'

'S'pose so,' said Lee and brushed off the hair-ruffle before standing up and pulling his pyjama jacket over his head. 'I just need a quick wash,' he said and disappeared into the bathroom.

'Oi, Lee,' said his father through the bathroom door, 'did he get a shiner too?'

*

The church clock was striking ten as Lee and his father made their way along the New Canal, towards their favourite spot, just beyond the lock.

The air was still warm, and midges hovered close to the surface. Get into a swarm of midges and you'd know it-in your hair, in your mouth, they got everywhere. But it was the only part of fishing that Lee really detested; everything else was brilliant, better than football even. He loved the peace and quiet of the canal with its overhanging branches and the way the gentle, dappled sunlight, and the moving shadows, played tricks with your eyes. School and all its problems faded quickly as they made their way past the tiny cottages not far from the lock. The cottages were old and uninhabited and the roofs had fallen in many years before, leaving only the shells of the buildings standing. Nettles and bindweed filled the spaces where, once-upon-a-time no doubt, families of workers talked, ate, and played cards together; now warning signs advised people to Keep Out! Danger of Falling Masonry. Cans

23

and broken beer bottles, left by those with nowhere better to go -some of them Lee's mates- added to the perils of the place. Lee picked up a pebble and shied it towards the rotting door of the nearest cottage, 'yessss-ing!' at the tinkle of breaking glass.

'Oi, Lee! Cut it out! Got to keep this place as it is- can't go round making a mess, and breaking stuff. I've told you that before.' His father glared at him, and he looked down sheepishly.

'Oh, yeah. Sorry, wasn't thinkin',' his son replied, and they trudged on in silence, lugging their fishing gear between them in a large canvas bag.

Ten minutes later, they arrived at their favourite spot beyond the quarry where Lee's dad reckoned the fishing was the best for miles around. As always, there was no-one else about, so they settled on a shady spot and put down the bag, which landed with a dull thud on the bank. Lee massaged his shoulder where the bag had rubbed it sore and he started to help his father unpack the gear. Setting up camp was a ritual - almost a holy one- and Lee knew that everything had to be positioned exactly right. Wayne was a locksmith and liked to know where every piece of equipment was—'tidy kit, tidy mind' was how he put it. In another five minutes they were sitting on their fold-down chairs, Wayne had put the kettle on, and they had hunkered down to see what they could catch

*

The next few hours were as peaceful a time as either of them could remember down by the canal. Very few people passed where they sat and dozed in the afternoon warmth, and those that did either said nothing or mumbled a quick 'afternoon' and went on their way. That's what it was like fishing by the canal; you were part of the world and its people, but somehow not quite a full part. People could see you, out in the fresh air, in a public place, but almost everyone respected your privacy. They seemed to know that you had come to this very spot for peace and quiet: just you, the water, the birds, and the fish. Well, sometimes the fish. It was a bit like being in your own private bubble.

'Ever read *Wind in the Willows*, in school Lee? It's a story book, all about animals who live by the river,' his dad asked, breaking the silence- eyes half-open, fishing hat tipped gently onto his nose.

Lee looked amazed. 'Nah-don't think so. Why?' he replied.

'Well, you know I'm not much of a one with books, but there's a bit I always remember from when we read it in school-you know, with the teacher at the end of the day. How did it go?' He concentrated hard and after a few seconds continued: '*All was a-shake and a-shiver, glints and gleams and sparkles,* and then something about *swirls* and *bubbles*. I loved that bit when I heard it first 'cos it reminded me of the water down here by the canal in summer. I used to think that even if I was never going to be a rich man, as long as I could be near water, no-one could ever take that feeling away from me…' Suddenly, the bell on Lee's rod started tinkling, signalling that something was on the other end of his line. The surface of the canal bubbled and fizzed as he started to reel in his catch and he asked himself what it would be this time. Probably a roach or trout- he'd caught two trout already that afternoon. He'd always dreamed of his reel screaming and his rod arching dangerously as he hooked his first pike, but in reality he had never got close. 'One day,' he thought, but reeling in the line he knew that today was not going to be it.

'It's another bloody stickleback Lee,' laughed his father as he repositioned his hat, helped him release the wriggling fish from the hook, and threw it back into the water. 'Let the pathetic tiddler live to fight another day, shall we? Time for a proper fish… and chips, and all the trimmings son. Let's pack up and get home while we're ahead.' Lee couldn't see how they were 'ahead' but he was weary and getting hungry too. The battered cod would be the only fish worth having today and the promise of food encouraged him to help his father collect everything quickly and head for home.

Near the cottages, and on the outside bank of a gentle curve, the rim of Clarke's Quarry was just visible. A heron, a flashback to prehistoric times, flew low over the pair and headed silently towards the long-defunct excavations. Some quarter of a mile across, the entrance had been gouged and blasted from the rock of the valley-side two centuries earlier, but now the quarry was a silent place. Long gone was the sharp crack of pick and shovel on chalk and flint, and the only sound to be heard today was the faint flapping of the heron's wings as it dipped over the still lake which occupied the quarry floor. Moorhens, and ducks too, busied themselves comically in their search for weed, and only rarely was the peace broken by the distress call of an unwary bird startled by a passing cyclist or noisy youngster.

Lee was tired as they trudged along the dusty towpath, passing the lock and the old lock-keeper's cottage, now converted into a small museum of sorts. This had been a great day with his dad-a lazy, happy time whose memories he would revisit in the short, dark days of winter. But it hadn't started off well, the previous school-week's shenanigans blighting much of his week and infecting his dreams. Passing the quarry, Lee's mind returned to a question which had built in importance over the recent months and which now was reaching a crescendo. It was something which as a kid he had always taken for granted, but which was now billowing like a dark storm cloud on a hot summer's day. It was something that as a younger child it had never occurred to him to ask his father about. In this village it was like wondering 'why is water wet, or iron heavy?' It just was. It just is.

He took a deep breath, sensing correctly it would be a question that his father would not welcome.

'Dad?'

'Yes, Lee.'

'You know the Uppers thing? And the Clarkes thing? Does anyone really know why we don't get on, or why we're supposed not to get on? And how comes it's us, the Parkers, who are sort of the main family on the Lowers side and the Parkers on the Uppers?' He kicked a pebble into the canal, and watched it sink out of sight with hardly a splash.

Wayne Parker carried on looking straight ahead and didn't seem to have heard.

'Dad?'

'Well, it's like this son,' he finally replied, his voice serious and a little distant. It's an old thing Lee, goes back years. It happens all over the world where one lot doesn't get on with another lot. Ends in wars sometimes. Whatever started it all off is a mystery- nobody knows and nobody really cares. It's all too late now to do anything about it. That's just Hensford. Uppers. Lowers. Clarkes. Parkers. A done deal, so don't go worrying about it. Just get on with your life and if they punch you, punch 'em back- no matter what your mum or Mr Whats'isname at school says.'

'Okay, but dad...'Lee tried to press him further.

His father stopped suddenly and whipped round to face him. 'Leave it son,' he repeated firmly, and, giving him the sort of look his own father would have been proud of, strode off towards fish, chips and home.

Chapter Three

October 1798
The Site of The New Canal - Hensford Village

The younger of the two men stopped digging, leant on his shovel, and wiped his brow with the sleeve of his jerkin. Despite the distinct chill in the air, this hard work was causing him to sweat profusely, so he reached for his leather bottle and took a long swig. The beer tasted foul, but helped to slake his almost permanent thirst.

'It's looking good Jethro. Won't be long now,' confirmed the other man as he also took a drink of his own favourite tipple-cognac, carried as always in his fancy hip flask, 'to keep out the chill.'

Edmund Clarke stood tall, surveyed the scene, and used his silver-topped cane to point at the different parts of the site: what was going well, what was causing him concern, which of his men needed a 'damn good kick up the breeches', and so on. He was a proud, ambitious man whose strong features left no-one in any doubt as to the strength of his resolve to get the job done, 'come Hell or high water'. A man of perhaps forty-five years he looked ten years older. A lifetime of rising with the lark and burning the midnight oil had made him the man he was today. 'Work hard-Play hard' was the rule he lived by, now in his later years making the most of the finer things in life that his riches allowed him to enjoy. But it *had* taken its toll and the lines in his face told their story as clearly as the lines in any one of the numerous books that filled the shelves of his private library. His dark, swept-back hair had turned to grey at the temples and his brow, at least whilst he was working, held a permanent frown.

All around them, gangs of men and boys-some as young as ten years old- sweated and cursed as bucket after bucket of heavy clay was passed from hand to hand from the base of the narrow channel and on to one of the rickety wooden wagons waiting to cart it away. Day after day, for years, the project had rumbled on but at last the end was finally in sight. Soon, some said within the year, God willing, the channel would be completed, and barges would take the place of ducks and moorhens in making the journey from the quarry to the Grand Junction Canal, now only a few hundred yards distant.

Edmund Clarke replaced his flask and consulted his gold watch that hung on a heavy chain from his wais'cot. He looked at the glowering skies and closed his topcoat a little more snugly around his collar. His tricorn hat and scarf kept out much of the chill; but the day still felt raw.

'Light's going Jethro. Let the men get back to their families. And get those horses fed and watered. They're going to need to keep going apace if we want to finish by the spring. Just think Jethro,' he mused, 'my very own canal to take Clarke's stone to help face the most elegant houses of London! The finest chalk to make the finest plaster for the best builders in the kingdom. It'll be a proud moment for the Clarkes and a turning point in the history of Hensford.'

'Indeed, Mr Clarke,' replied the man in the hole and dug his shovel hard into the soft clay- the clay which clung to everything-to tools, to boots, to breeches and to the matted hair of the wretched horses which plodded their way, come rain or shine, along the towpath of what would be called 'The Hensford Arm'. By the standards of the 1790's this would be a short stretch of new water. Tens, rather than hundreds, of men, and mostly local at that, had toiled and grafted to ensure that Hensford would not be left behind in the drive for riches. A new century was about to dawn and Edmund Clarke was determined that he would join the likes of Mr Josiah Wedgewood and Mr James Watt in enjoying the lavish rewards of the new age. He, his family, and perhaps even a few of the local men he employed, would enjoy considerably better futures because of *his* vision and his ambition. 'Clarke's of Hensford: Stone- merchants of Distinction', would be known as far afield as the great cities of London, Birmingham, Bristol and Manchester. Hensford would be, quite literally, put on the map and it would all be down to him, Edmund Clarke Esquire, self-made man.

As he turned for home he raised his cane and bade his foreman good-day. The clay beneath his feet was no respecter of fine leather and his boots squelched and slithered as he walked, with as much dignity as he could muster, towards his waiting carriage and its four black stallions. Jethro Parker was certainly uneducated, like all the men, but Edmund Clarke held a grudging respect for his foreman. The men seemed to like him well enough too and knew that whatever he was asking them to do he would expect himself to do likewise. Jethro was seen as one of the men. A Hensford man through and through, he had earned their respect through hard work and the skilful negotiations he had conducted with Mr Clarke and the others who owned shares in the canal- many of whom were from beyond the valley and seemed only to understand the language of profit and loss.

For his part too, Jethro Parker respected-almost liked, he would say- his boss and master. Jethro understood his place in the greater scheme of things of course but, nevertheless, felt pride in his own contribution to what would be a major step forward in the long history of Hensford and its people. The Parkers had lived in the village for as long as anyone could remember-and probably a great deal longer than that, besides. He may not be a man of letters but people looked up to him, trusted him and knew him to be a good foreman: firm but fair. He waited until he saw his boss's carriage round the corner and disappear into the gloom of the early evening and then, with some difficulty, mounted the side of the hole that had been his place of work for most of the afternoon. Raising a whistle to his lips, he sounded the end of the day's shift and the noise of digging and heaving was replaced by the murmur and grumble of men downing tools, searching for their pipes of clay and pouches of rough-cut tobacco. Here and there, the gloom was pierced by the jump of a spark and a smoky wraith-like glow as men lit-up and started their walk home, shoulders hunched against the deepening chill.

Emerging from a nearby trench, Jethro's eldest son, William, walked wearily towards his father. His day was by *no* means over as he would be responsible for leading the horses to their stables and ensuring they were fed and watered, ready for the coming night. Thirteen years old with the same wiry frame and sharp, dark features as his father, Will took great pride in this position of trust. Unusually for the time, the boy looked on the animals not as beasts of burden but as friends to be nurtured and loved. He had a countryman's instinct that told him what a towns-person would never understand: that if you care and tend to the needs of a working animal they will repay you may times over. A sick, lame horse is no good to any worker, he would tell you, fit only for the knackers' yard, while a horse well looked after will be a trusted servant and will give you the best years of its life. 'And besides,' he thought, 'I like them better than I do people; most of the time at least.'

'Will, my boy, you're a good lad. I'll help with the horses tonight. Looks like a storm's a-comin' and we don't want to catch our deaths out here, do we?'

'I'd be much obliged, dad,' replied the boy , and the two walked, arms around each other's shoulders, to where two of

Will's favourites animals steamed and stamped at the end of a hard day's graft. Will rubbed the muzzle of the larger of the two, a Chestnut-coloured Suffolk Punch named Bess, who shook her shaggy mane and tossed her head in appreciation. Careful not to show favouritism, he patted the glistening flanks of Silver, a powerful grey mare, who shuffled impatiently in the knowledge, Will was sure, that a rubdown and a long-awaited meal of oats and hay was just around the corner.

Slowly, father and son walked the plodding, snorting pair along the muddy path they had come to know so well over the preceding months, a long line of tired horses following dutifully behind. Indeed, had they let go of the wet reins, the leading pair would have taken themselves and the others back to the makeshift stables, some half a mile from where they now were. Not much was said between Will and his father as they walked-it had been a long, hard day and neither was in the mood for small-talk. That could wait until later when they would sit as a family around their simple table, thank God for the food they were about to receive, and address the hunger that was now starting to gnaw at the pit of their bellies.

Will tended to the horses while Jethro watched with a certain pride as the men he knew and loved trudged towards their draughty dwellings. 'Night Jethro!' they called as they filed past ,the foreman acknowledging them each by name- Alfred, Bill, Jack, Edward.., all good men, hard-working and loyal, with families of their own to feed and clothe in these hard times. How much would *they* benefit from the new channel? thought Jethro, as the last of the men bade him good-night. 'Not the place of a man like me to worry me'self about such things-just get on with the job in-hand,' he mused, as he and Will finally turned into the wind and followed his men along the muddy path towards the stone cottage that the Parker family called home.

*

The cottage was small and sturdy, but even at this time of the year, cold : not a great deal warmer than the autumn air outside. But, it *was* dry, and when Elizabeth Parker got the fire burning brightly in the hearth, passably comfortable, and certainly more so than the mean dwellings lived in by her husband's men.

As the darkness fell Elizabeth busied herself, dividing her time between looking after Will's young brother and sisters and making sure the food would be ready when 'the men' returned from their day in the ditches. Most days, she and the younger children would spend their time at the local plaiters' school where all were employed in the business of plaiting straw for the hat-makers of nearby Luton. The hours were long but the wages, however meagre, helped to provide the family with the necessities of life- the rent for their cottage, fresh vegetables from the village market, and the occasional piece of meat when they could afford it. Lizzie could earn as much as sixteen or seventeen shillings in a good week and even little Rose was learning fast and could bring home a quarter of that amount. But the room in which they worked was small, twelve feet square at most, and they shared the space with as many as twenty others. In the winter they froze, and they were rarely without colds; in the summer heat they sweltered and prayed once more for the cool of autumn to give them some relief.

A hard rat-a-tat-tat at the door signalled the workers' return, and Elizabeth gestured to Rose, eight years old and her mother's little helper, to pull back the bolt and let her father and brother in. The bolt was old and rusted and it was with some difficulty that the girl freed the latch which allowed Jethro and Will to finally come home for the night. Jethro bent to kiss the top of his daughter's head and she in turn hugged his legs and ran back to where she was playing with her straw-doll, the only plaything she could truly call her own. The oil lamp in the centre of the room gave off a weak light adding just a little to the smoky glow of the wood burning in the hearth. Jethro and Will greeted the rest of the family before warming their hands by the crackling fire.

'Smells good, Lizzie,' commented the man of the house as he stared into the flames. 'Fair famished we are-isn't that right Will?'

'I could eat a horse -but as you well know mother, I wouldn't!' replied her son smiling as he took off his cap and slumped on one of the four chairs placed around the rough wooden table.

'I managed to get a little ox-tail,' said Elizabeth returning the smile, and pushed a lock of hair away from her hazel eyes. 'Not a lot, but enough to make a tasty stew- I mixed it up well with what we had in the way of potatoes and carrots from the garden. Enough to keep The Devil from the door for another night, anyways.'

'Sounds just fine, Elizabeth,' said Jethro and gave her arm a reassuring squeeze before settling down next to his son at the table. In the grate a blazing log crackled loudly and a spark jumped onto the stone hearth. Making ends meet was never easy but Lizzie ran the household wisely. She was good woman-a faithful wife and a loving mother and Jethro knew he had much to be grateful for. And so every night, before blowing out the candle at their bedside, he thanked the Lord for his good fortune and begged Him to keep them safe until the break of day. He was a God-fearing man and had brought up his children to believe likewise-church and Sunday school without fail, grace at meals and a little Bible reading whenever time allowed. The Bible, the only book in the house, took pride of place on the shelf above the fire. It stood next to a roughly carved cross and a small cracked jug which Elizabeth would fill with wild flowers and blossom as the seasons allowed: Daffodils in the spring, Moon Daisies and Cornflowers in summer, Herb Robert and Forget-me-not signified autumn had arrived, and red-berried Holly marked the shortening days of winter and the approach of Christmas. Jethro himself had had scant education but Sunday school had taught him to read a little and he even knew some important passages by heart. His faith gave him hope for the future and he made sure that all his children were also versed in the stories and poetry of the Holy Book. Will was now at an age when fishing or hunting rabbits in the fields exerted a more powerful pull than the hard cold of the Sunday school classroom and on occasion he would be allowed out early from classes; but he was his father's son and knew he would one day be head of his own family, and needed to be well-educated in the ways of The Lord.

Elizabeth removed the heavy iron pot from the fire and began to ladle the steaming broth onto wooden plates and bowls, all of different shapes and sizes. None of the fine Wedgewood china crockery that graced the table of the Clarke's mansion, high upon the hill, for this family. But then, no man, rich or poor, would enjoy his food more than Jethro on this dark autumn's evening, and that, as he turned from the fire to the table, gave him great comfort. The younger children-Rose, and four-year old Daniel - would eat where they played on the rush-covered floor. Baby Jane, sleeping fitfully in her crib, would wake when hungry and be soothed by a little milk and mash made from the stew so eagerly awaited by her older brothers and sister. The shortening of the days had confused the mite and rare was the night when the family slept for more than an hour or two before waking to her mewling cries. Sharing as they did the single space that was their kitchen, living room, and bedroom, little privacy was to be had, and when sickness struck it was usual for the six of them to suffer as one. But still, they were grateful to their maker for what they had in a loving family, for the food in their bellies and for the roof over their heads.

The older Parkers sat around the little table, closed their eyes and bowed silently. Jethro, head of the family, clasped his hands in prayer and began: 'For what we are about to receive may the good Lord make us truly thankful. Amen.' William and Elizabeth echoed the final word in chorus and the meal was started in the flickering half-light of the fire. Jethro and Elizabeth exchanged what little news they had of the goings-on in the village; the tittle-tattle at the water-pump, who was sick, and whatever stories had come from beyond the valley in which Hensford nestled. In hushed tones Elizabeth told how she had heard at plaiters' school of another stagecoach held up by a gang of masked highwaymen, no more than a few minutes ride along the road from The Land of Plenty Inn in Upper Hensford. She started to describe the terror of the attack and how pistols had been used to rob the petrified passengers of any valuables they carried. Sharply, Jethro looked across at his wife and held up a hand, gesturing for her to stop, mid-story.

'Can't have the little uns being afeared to close their eyes tonight, Lizzie,' he whispered, 'but it is a bad state of affairs when honest men and defenceless women-folk cannot have safe passage about the King's lanes and highways. Those villains deserve never to see the light of day and...and may God have mercy on their souls,' he mumbled, remembering the compassion he had learned as part of his Christian upbringing.

He wiped his plate with a piece of rough brown bread torn from a loaf, and drank deep from a jug of beer placed at the centre of the table. This time the beer tasted good-here, in the warmth of his own house, sitting next to his faithful wife, surrounded by his loving children.

Two hours later, with the fire a guttering glow, the family was asleep. Jethro snored loudly, Elizabeth pulled the rough blanket a little closer, and in her basket Jane whimpered gently as her tummy grumbled and her eyelids began to flicker open once again.

Chapter Four

Wednesday September 15th 2010
The Staffroom - Hensford High School

'Good holiday Dave?' It was Charles from the maths department.

'D'you mean that one a million years ago, Chas? Yeah, not bad. Low key really -didn't get away, except to see the folks back home. Filial duty and all that.'

'I suppose you spent most of your time up to your eyeballs in paint and wallpaper paste-making a hovel out of a slum.'

'Oi! An Englishman's home is his castle so my place has got to be a fort, or a keep, at least. And I know it isn't in the best part of town.'

'Town?'

'But it's mine, and I *love* it.'

'Okay, fair do's. I swear never to take the piss again! And what about the tutor group: 8S I believe?'

'Again, not bad. Interesting mix- the good, the bad and the ugly, really. Uppers and Lowers split down the middle and ne'er the twain shall meet. Especially the boys. Oh, and I've got the two lads- Parker and Clarke, so that's been a bit tasty on occasions.'

'Ooh, I say!' Charles Farnon rubbed his hands with glee. 'And in the red corner...'

'No. No fights this year so far, but Big Ted has asked me to keep an eye on them and he's kindly suggested that I try to do something *extra-curricular* with them on the *particular issues confronting the youth of the village.* Something *historical, maybe.'*

'Ooh,good one! More like something hysterical, Dave!' Charles said, warming to his theme. 'You could do a re-enactment- like one of those ones where two dozen nutters dressed as Saxons lob things at a bunch of blokes in Norman armour. What could you call it? Upstairs and Downstairs-no, too prissy. How about War& Peace? Been done before. Le Crunch-too ...'

David stopped him mid-flow. 'Okay, Chas, thanks for that most helpful contribution to the historical canon. When the maths department wants advice on how to teach The Calculus or differential equations to bottom set year 9, then I'm your man.'

'Christ Dave! Thanks for reminding me! I've got their books to mark by next lesson. Not calculus but guzzintas.'

'Guzzintas?'

'Yeah, you know, three guzzinta twelve, four times... that sort of thing. Must dash!'

'Pint later?'

'Not today mate-another time, eh? Got to go.'

David stretched his legs under the coffee table and threw his head back to look at the ceiling. One of the strip lights flickered on and off annoyingly- probably a deliberate attempt by management to cut down on staffroom chat, he thought. Maybe a re-enactment wasn't such a crazy idea... Yes it was! What was he thinking! And what was there to 're-enact' anyway? Maybe a slot or two in his form's PHSE programme could be devoted to the Uppers and Lowers question, but who was to know into what deep and dangerous waters it would take them? He was certain that greater minds than his had been brought to bear on the situation in the past but to what avail? He'd just have to be patient, see what came along, and take it from there.

Chapter Five

Thursday September 16th 2010
Big Ted's Office

Big Ted looked at the boys through reddened eyes. The previous night he'd had one too many at The Feathers, attracted by the pub's Sky sports and real ale rather than its dubious clientele. Well-named, Ted was a man of massive proportions and if lugubriousness were a political ideology, he would have been its party leader.

'Right. Who's going to start?' He stared at the boys' faces, his eyes moving first to one, then the other. Neither boy spoke. Alex fiddled with his cuff while Lee's leg drummed up and down in nervous anticipation.

Ted unfolded the scrap of paper he'd been handed by the mid-day supervisor. 'Okay, Alex, it just says *'Fight'*. You start- never been backwards in coming forwards, and as I haven't got all day, you can kick off.'

Alex looked up and searched the ceiling for an answer.

'Well, it really started because of the cricket match last summer.'

'Before the holidays?'

'Yes, sir.'

'Right,' the teacher sighed. 'Dramatic victory for the lowers was it?' he asked, leaning forward onto his huge, freckled forearms. 'Something I should have read about on the back pages of The Observer, maybe?'

'Not exactly, Mr Richards,' said Alex tentatively, 'more of a hammering by the Uppers really. *Business as usual* is what my dad said.'

'Yeah, only 'cos you lot practised the whole time and had all the gear,' Lee blurted out, to be silenced, instantly, with just a look from his head of year.

'Right. Cricket. Not my favourite. So what happened? I'll try to stay awake.'

'Well, I was first bat and Lee was doing the bowling. The first bowl I took just on the bounce and I sort of hooked it, and when Mr Taylor, he's the head of science...'

'Yeah, I know who Mr Taylor is,' Ted interrupted, 'and I don't need a match report either Alex, thank you. Get to the point. Why did you two have a fight?' He pinched the flesh between his eyes.

'Well, Lee, him, deliberately threw a ball at me and missed my head by *this* much!' Alex indicated a couple of inches between his thumb and his first finger.

'That's crap Alex! I missed you by miles *and* it was an accident.'

'I've told you before- don't start again Lee! I'll let you speak in a minute, now zip it!'

'Yes Mr Richards,' said Lee and sank back into his chair.

'Right. Now Master Parker, it's *your* turn. Alex- no interrupting.' Alex nodded.

'He's sort of right, Sir, but it wasn't all my fault. I did throw the ball but I didn't know you couldn't. We'd only done a couple of lessons in year 7 and in my *old* school we played rounders. Any anyway, when it was our turn to bat, all of them-*including* Alex- were laughing and smirking, like we were babies who didn't understand anything. It wasn't funny and then all their parents and our parents got into a bit of bother, and I hate the game and never want to play it again-*ever*.'

'Right. So why did the fight just now start? Lee, as you seem to have found your voice, you can begin this time.' He turned a little in Lee's direction.

Lee took a deep breath then looked across at Alex. 'Well, it was after lunch. We was playing *football* and, surprise surprise, my team was about a million-nil up when the whistle went.'

Alex muttered something under his breath, but instantly fell quiet when he felt the teacher's eyes were on him.

'So, as we are walking in, just near the main doors, Alex barges me and I barge him back. Next thing I know we're on the floor with loads of people cheering and egging us on. He's definitely punched me in the face and I got a few good uns in on him too. Then someone dragged us off each other and I realised it was Mr Stacey and we got sent in with the dinner lady- first me, and then him. And then we came into your office.'

Mr Richards raised his eyebrows at Alex who nodded in agreement. 'Yeah, that's about it I suppose.'

'So, all over a game of cricket? The most exciting part really. So, what's to be done?'

Ted always finished his chats with this question. First, he thought, *boys would be boys*. Second, he didn't see why he should do all the thinking. It was a hot day, he had a headache, and ideas were thin on the ground. Third, and most important, he sincerely just couldn't be arsed. This was yet another example of Uppers v. Lowers, a dispute the UN peace-keeping force wouldn't take on and one he had absolutely no intention of involving himself in.

'Boys?'

They waited a full half-minute before one of them spoke.

'We could avoid each other?'

'Great idea Lee. Let's leave it at that. No more fighting, eh?'

'No, Mr Richards,' the boys answered in unison.

'Well off you go then...' The teacher stopped them before they disappeared through the door. 'Wait! You're both in 8P, right?' The boys confirmed that this was indeed the case. He strained, twisting his chair around to look at the large multi-coloured chart behind his desk. 'Let's see, 8P, 8P...gotcha! As I thought: Mr Stacey's your form tutor and he's also teaching you history. So maybe *he* can do something with you. Right, off you go- be good!'

Chapter Six

Saturday September 25th 2010
David's Flat

The phone rang and David made himself comfortable with his cup of filtered coffee and warm *pain au chocolate*, his Saturday morning treat. It would be his dad checking up, as he always did at this time, on how his son was getting along.

'Hi dad, how's things?'

'Oh, can't complain Dave. Back's been playing me up a bit so I guess I'll have to give up on the gymnastics. No, it's the gardening actually- all that weeding doesn't do me any good. Anyway, it's you I want to talk about. How's the second, or is it the third week, been?'

David filled his father in on the antics of the previous five days, describing in detail a selection of the most notable examples of bizarre or difficult behaviour ('and some of the kids were just as bad!') before asking his advice about how he should tackle the challenge Big Ted, Mr Richards, had presented him as a new year's gift.

'Tricky one that Dave ...not easy at all.' David could picture his father rubbing his chin and frowning, drumming his fingers, even, on the rosewood table where the phone normally sat. 'I'll give it some thought. Anyhow, you must be up to your eyeballs in paint and wall-paper paste!' he said, hoping for a clear change of direction.

'Have you been speaking to Charles?'

'Charles? Charles who? Don't know anyone called Charles? Should I?' said his father, now clearly confused.

'No, never mind dad, it's fine,' David laughed, 'just something you said.'

*

David picked up his rucksack and locked the door behind him. The hill was a steep one and the view it gave of the valley acted as a pick-me-up at the end of a long week. It was still early, the threat of bumping into pupils and parents slight, so he walked with the air of someone on holiday, an inquisitive visitor perhaps, more than that of the resident he actually was. Most shopping trips he did by car, not noticing the wealth of details he saw today, as he made his way down slowly, on foot. A public footpath, partly hidden by an overgrown privet, disappeared to the right while an old red post-box with *VR* embossed on its door was conveniently located a mere two hundred yards from his flat; tucked away and out of sight. The houses played a similar game of hide and seek, the majority hidden from view by well-established hedges or some type of evergreen that David couldn't quite place. Now and again, a quaint cottage, fringed with wisteria, poked its nose dangerously close to the road, inviting passers-by to look through the small windows in to the musty dark of a chintz-lined parlour. And in other places the twentieth century brashly announced its arrival in the form of satellite dishes, the geometric shapes and metallic surfaces jarring with the warmth of brick and stone onto which they clung.

And as the hill met the flat valley bottom, houses gave way to shops, giving David an excuse to saunter a-while, stopping occasionally to see what the local vendors had to offer. Mixed in with the bargain basements and take-aways the odd window caught his eye, and he made a note to visit one particularly interesting place, stocking everything from brooms and bowls to cups and saucers- exactly what a new flat owner needed. Another shop, complete with an old-looking sign in the shape of a hanging key, proclaimed itself to be *Parker's Locksmiths- Est 1968-The Key to Success!* 'I wonder', he thought, before moving on.

The little newsagents on the corner of the High Street and Albert Crescent was open, its window crammed with an array of cheap plastic toys, London Bus fridge-magnets, and any number of cards offering everything from gardening services to a sofa for sale: fifteen pounds. David walked in and helped himself to a bottle of ice-cold water and a bar of chocolate. The shopkeeper, a small Asian lady in a plain sari and grey, knitted cardigan, seemed to know him and asked if he worked at the high school.

'I have seen you on a number of occasions- outside, when I collect my grand-daughter,' she said, smiling, and handing over his change.

'What's her name-your grand-daughter?'

'She's Seema, Seema Patel. Year Ten. You know her?'

'Yeah, I know Seema-she's a nice girl'

'It's a good school?' she asked, and David assured her it was.

'It's got lots of good kids and, of course, *fantastic* teachers!'

This, it seems, was just the answer she wanted and she waved him on his way, but not before directing him to the end of the terrace and to the narrow alley-way which led from the street to the canal.

The alley itself was dark, Victorian, flanked on both sides by the red-brick gables of the adjacent terraces; but in a few moments David was emerging again, now walking the length of the long gardens which pointed him in the direction of the water, a couple of hundred yards away. Between the broken wooden fences and the chain-link, which ran in parallel, lay the detritus of youth, no different from that which he had grown up with in his own area of Muswell Hill: empty drink cans, crisp packets stuffed into gaps, free newspapers. And condoms of course-used. To make things worse, you had to watch where you stepped. David hurried through, glad to reach the patch of waste ground, an excuse for a field, a no-man's land between the town and the canal itself. To his right, three low-rise blocks of flats stood sentinel, concrete and glass reminders of the folly that the sixties brought. Or, they may have been from the following decade, David mused, testament to man's reluctance, inability even, to learn from his mistakes, however blindingly-obvious they might appear with the benefit of hindsight. Across the waste ground, in an open stair-well, he noticed a group of rusting bikes leaning together, their handlebars intertwined and supportive, like the arms of drunks helping each other to stand; and out of a hedge poked another- like a ram, held by its horns.

As he reached the kissing gate which led to the towpath, he heard a girl's voice, his name being called from somewhere in the direction of the flats.

'Mr Stacey! Sir!'

He scanned the buildings.

'I'm up here. Third floor!'

A hand flapped through the bottom of an open window-UPVC, white, hinged at the top and limited in the extent it could move. David strained to see through the glass to the person within, but it was impossible.

'Oh, hi! I can see you.'

'I live here.' The hand tapped at the concrete.

'I sort of gathered that.'

'Where you going?'

'For a walk. Up the canal.' He pointed.

'Why?'

'Well,...'

But before he could explain, another voice from inside the flat cut across and interrupted their conversation, someone shouting at the child, impatient and annoyed.

'Bye. Got to go! Have a good walk!'

Then with a bang the window closed and the hand was gone.

*

The sign said 'London 42 miles'. David turned the other way and started walking. A mixture of wood smoke and diesel gave the air a distinctively acrid smell that was both unpleasant and pleasant at the same time. It was the diesel that took him back to university days when he spent several carefree weeks working for a local builder with whom his dad had links. 'Start up the concrete mixer, Dave. You've got A levels,' the others would josh him, then leave him alone before settling down to their first brew of the day. 'Thirsty work Dave, got to keep your strength up!' they'd add seriously, and he'd wonder how on earth anything ever actually got built in this country. David, lost in his thoughts, was almost too late to step out of the way of a pair of mountain-bikers, who pinged at him several times before racing past and giving their grudging thank-yous.

The variety of canal-boats surprised him. All shapes, all sizes, some beautifully adorned with pictures and gold lettering, some coal-black and filthy. Heavy metal rubbed alongside classical. It was a jumble, a rich mix, the twee and the earthy cheek by jowl. No Uppers and no Lowers here, he said to himself.

Here and there, boat-owners had already emerged and sat, enjoying the still air of the morning. Breakfast smells mixed with that coming from the chimneys and David reached for his chocolate, wishing now that he himself had had an egg, or a bacon sandwich before he left his flat. A number of engines chugged away quietly. Bubbles appeared and disappeared in a strangely soothing parade at the boats' blunt ends, as David thought of the sterns- what would his dad say! One or two boats were already on their way and every owner, to a man, returned his greeting with an exaggerated wave and some comment on it being a lovely day for it. David felt good; glad that he'd left his marking in the boot.

It wasn't long, however, before he came across what he had been looking for. The moorings had come to an end and some half a mile further on he stopped outside a small white building, an old lock-keeper's cottage, with the words 'Adam's Lock Museum' painted above the door. Nearby, a narrowboat was negotiating its way through the gates of the eponymous lock and a small group of ducks paddled its way to the safety of the bank.

A low white wall and a flimsy wooden gate separated the building from the towpath. He opened the gate and tried the door-handle to find it locked, then stepped back to look for some indication of when it might be open. Another sign, a handwritten post-card cellotaped to the window, told him that this was:

The Adam's Lock Canal Museum

Open Mon, Wed & Thurs and the last Saturday of the month

9am till 3-ish

Contact: Mrs D Huggins on 01324 785306

Groups Welcome!

He took out his phone and took a picture.

Between the window and the towpath a collection of old iron tools caught his eye, secured together on the ground or fixed to the wall of the cottage, framing the door and windows like pieces of an abstract work of art. Pliers and pincers, hammers, tongs and the fused links of a heavy iron chain were solid reminders of the canal's industrial past. These were the tools of days gone-by, when wood and metal were shaped by the sweat and toil of workers' hands. David knelt and ran his hands over the smooth black-painted surfaces and wondered at the stories they could tell, if only they were able to speak.

Getting up, he leant at the windows but could see little more than a small room: more like a café or bookshop than a museum, he thought. He took one last look round the back but, finding nothing to see, he decided to take a few more pictures, then head for home.

Back to his flat and the mountain of marking that he knew would be waiting for him.

Chapter Seven

May 28th 1799
The New Canal

A crowd of several hundred had assembled on the canal bank with most sitting near the lock where the ceremony would take place. The air was thick with the smell of an ox roasting upon a spit, the slowly sizzling hub of the banquet laid on by Mr Clarke to mark this special day. A group of villagers danced around a maypole specially bedecked with flowers, and nearby a small stage had been set up for an opening ceremony that many of the locals thought they might never see. The fair-weather clouds that cast fleeting shadows upon the gathering did nothing to spoil the festival atmosphere as children ran excitedly up and down the towpath, shouting loudly and waving bright Union Flags. Wealthy men in short wigs and fine country clothes bowed low to elegant ladies with parasols, tipping their top-hats respectfully as they made their way towards the staging: a stage from which Mr Clarke would say his thank-yous before Mr Chambers, Mayor of Hensford, finally declared the New Canal open. The children of ordinary village-folk stared open-mouthed at the sight of well-to-do families in their finery, here for the day from their big houses and estates high on the valley sides and beyond: gentleman farmers like Thomas Lucas and Edward Barr, and others who stood to increase their fortunes by taking full advantage of the new links to London and the North. These were the men of substance and their families who, although they visited the lower valley as infrequently as possible, could not miss out on this occasion and the opportunity to be seen rubbing shoulders with the great and good of Hensford. In contrast, the sons and daughters of Jack Aldred, Bill Fossey, and the other canal workers were reminded to watch their manners, stop staring, and remember their place- but carried on gawping, regardless.

Jethro Parker and his family arrived early and took their place next to the staging itself. Lizzie had opened a small hamper of homemade food that she had been preparing for several days- the best she could afford. 'Have to present us in the best light we can, Jethro,' she whispered to her husband, when questioned about the expense. 'Greatest day in the Parker family history- the proudest day of my life and I want people to know it,' she added. She leant over, straightened his collar and smoothed out the creases in his jacket, the very same one he had worn to his wedding day fifteen years earlier. Jethro smiled, and thanked her for being 'the rock on which our family is built', then made his way to the stage where Edmund Clarke and Mayor Chambers were just now mounting the steps.

'Jethro, my friend, welcome!' Mr Clarke offered his hand to his foreman and introduced him to the mayor; needlessly, as it happened, as they knew each other well from Sunday services at the village church of St James'.

'Jethro Parker- you should be a proud man to be part of this, the most important day in Hensford for many a long year!' said the mayor as he also shook him warmly by the hand.

Jethro cleared his throat and, thanking the mayor for his kind words, made it very clear that he was but a small player and that all praise should go to the man behind it all-his boss, Mr Edmund Clarke. In turn, Edmund Clarke Esquire acknowledged his foreman's comments with a small bow of his head before leading both to the edge of the stage which over-looked the large crowd gathered around the lock.

He raised his hands above his head, the talk of adults and the squeals of excited children gradually dying away. All eyes then turned toward the trio standing upon the stage, waiting to get the ceremony underway. Mr Clarke paused further until the hush was absolute then spoke, forceful and proud, the emotion of the day occasionally making itself heard in an over-long silence or tell-tale crack in his voice.

'My dear people of Hensford!' he began.

A cheer went up forcing the quarry owner, now canal-builder, to stop and wait for a full minute until the noise subsided and his words could be heard again.

'My dear people-thankyou! This is indeed a great day, not only for the men and women of our village but also for me and my family. It has been a long road that we have travelled but here we are today, together, near its end. And where one road finishes another starts, to take us to places as yet unvisited-nay, perhaps, undreamed of! And yet this is no ordinary 'road' that we see ahead of us. This canal, The Hensford Arm, will lead us out of our secluded valley to who knows where? The lime from our quarry, rough as it may look to the untrained eye, will grace some of the finest, most beautiful buildings in the land. In time, King George himself may think himself fortunate to live amongst the grandest squares and most elegant avenues of London, bearing the unmistakeable mark of the Hensford village quarry!'

At this, a second and more prolonged cheer went up, with some shouts of 'God Save the King' whilst others echoed with 'God bless Mr Clarke' and other, similar, sentiments. Once again Edmund Clarke, his customary frown replaced by a rare, benign smile, raised his hands above his head and waited for the chance to resume his speech.

'Before I ask our Mayor, Mr Chambers, to cut this ribbon and declare the canal open, I want to express the gratitude of my dear wife, Charlotte, and our children Adam, David and little Jane, hiding there behind her mother's skirts. And to each and every one of you, thank you *all* for your hard work and dedication. The canal was finished ahead of time, with few delays, and in time for this beautiful English summer's day!' He spread his arms wide and turned to every corner of the crowd, making sure everyone present felt it was to them personally that his thanks was directed.

Again, a ripple of applause as the working men and women of the village accepted the recognition that was theirs. 'And particular appreciation must go to the man on my right, Mr Jethro Parker, who has led you through sun, rain and snow to this wonderful moment. Thank *you*, Jethro!'

At this a number of men stood up and cheered, some throwing their hats into the air whilst clapping the foreman in his moment of glory. Jethro, unused to such attention, shuffled his feet, but smiled and nodded in the direction of 'his men'.

'And finally, on this most momentous of days, and as gesture of my eternal gratitude to you, my proud men, I intend to mark the culmination of your years of hard work, with an annual gift to the good people of Hensford. Each year, on this very day, and for as long as I am able, I shall arrange a party, a day of feasting, music and dancing to keep alive the memory of this wonderful and historic event!'

Once again, a loud cheer went up from every corner of the assembled crowd, although many men were at the same time reminded that the work which had kept their families fed, and which had provided a roof over their heads for the past three years, would be no more. At the dawn of a new century, a century which promised so much to the likes of the Clarkes and their kind, what hope for the common man and his family? But today was time for celebration-to eat, drink, and be merry, and to trust in the good Lord to provide.

'And on that happy note I call on Daniel Chambers, Mayor of Hensford in the county of Hertfordshire, on this day, the 28th of May in the year of Our Lord seventeen hundred and ninety-nine, to cut the ribbon and declare the canal open for business.'

A ribbon stretched from the stage to the far side of the canal, and a barge, full to the gunnels with Clarke's Quarry Limestone, waited for the signal to be the first of many to pass this spot on the way to the building sites of London Town. The mayor stepped to the front where he could be seen more clearly and, making the most of the occasion, held aloft a large pair of silver ceremonial scissors for all the crowd to see.

'It gives me great pleasure,' he announced proudly, 'to declare the New Canal, the Hensford Arm, well and truly open!' and with a theatrical flourish snipped the red, white, and blue ribbon, which fell fluttering into the still waters of the channel.

The crowd cheered once more and with a shout of 'Walk On!' the horse towing the first of many barges to come, tossed its head and started its steady pull towards the greatest city of the British Empire. Children waved their flags, and proud working men everywhere raised their tankards in a loud salute to a job well done, whilst on stage the three men shook hands vigorously, their wives and families looking on with obvious pride.

The local band struck up a rousing chorus of 'God Save the King!' at which some of the smaller children covered their ears and wailed horribly. This was to be the start of the biggest party Hensford had ever seen and one which would last well into the small hours of the following day. Some men, drunk on the ale that flowed, and heady from the excitement of the day, would argue and fight each other whilst one -a certain James Lee- would fall blindly into the canal to be pulled, cursing and shivering, to the safety of the bank by a group of laughing on-lookers.

On leaving the platform, Mr Clarke joined his foreman and his family on the grassy verge, but declined Lizzie's offer of something to eat. He enquired after the health of Mrs Parker and the children before walking Jethro away from the family so that they could speak in private.

'Well Jethro, it's been three years of hard graft but with my money and the sweat of you and your good men we've done it. They said it couldn't –then it wouldn't -be done, but by God we proved them wrong.'

'Indeed, Mr Clarke, we've all got a lot to be proud of, and a lot to be thankful for. But without your vision and your resolve I fear we would never have even made a start to this great project,' replied Jethro. Over the shoulder of his boss he saw friends and workmates talking, eating, and dancing, and watched as the first barge of chalk disappeared round a distant bend in the canal.

'So, what does the future hold for you and your family Jethro?' asked Mr Clarke, and stood, hands clasped behind his back, looking directly at his foreman.

'I don't rightly know, Mr Clarke,' replied Jethro, his eyes turned to the horizon. 'But something is sure to come my way. Maybe another canal to be dug. Or perhaps a fine house to be built. Using Clarke's lime, of course'

'Who's to say?' he added positively, but feared in his heart that today could be the last day of work for a long time to come.

'Jethro,' said the other man seriously, 'I have a proposition to make.'

'A proposition, Mr Clarke?'

'Yes, Jethro, a proposition. You see, I'm going to need a lock-keeper to ensure the smooth flow of barges up and down the new canal. Someone who knows the area well- someone familiar with the canal, the village, its people. It would come with the new cottage- room enough for you and your family- and pay enough to keep you all warm, dry and well fed for the rest of your days. It's a job of responsibility, Jethro, and I need someone I can trust. I need a dependable worker, you understand. And I think you could be the very man.' He paused to allow his foreman to think a moment. 'So Jethro, what do you say?'

Jethro looked over to where his wife and William sat and where his younger children played upon the grass. He thought of the cottage in which they now lived-small and cramped and difficult to heat in winter; but their home, nevertheless. Then he looked across the canal to where the Lock-Keeper's cottage stood, newly built and empty, waiting for its first occupants. Built of granite and roofed with slate it would make a grand house for him and his growing family. It was even rumoured to have a cooking range and two separate rooms for sleeping. How could he refuse? He straightened up and not for the first time that afternoon, cleared his throat to speak.

'I would be most honoured to be the first lock-keeper on your new canal Mr Clarke!' he beamed, and shook his boss's outstretched hand as a sign of acceptance.

'And I too am most pleased Jethro, and look forward to your service for many years to come. But there is just one more thing I need to add.'

'Yes, Mr Clarke?' said Jethro, not daring to guess what might be coming next.

'Have you ever been to Barnet Fair, Jethro?'

'Never, Mr Clarke,' he replied, bemused.

'Then you and your son, William, shall join me and my son, Adam, on our next trip to the town. I need to visit in the autumn- to take the waters, buy a few items for Mrs Clarke and the house and, well, just to enjoy the hurly-burly of the fair. Do I take it that my new lock-keeper, with his eldest son and heir, would be happy to accept my generous offer?' He smiled again and touched Jethro on his arm.

'Absolutely, sir! We would be *most* honoured to join you. Thank you, from the bottom of my heart Mr Clarke,' he said, shaking his hand vigorously, 'and now may I be excused so that I can tell my wife and children what great fortune we have had this day?'

'With my blessing,' replied Mr Clarke and watched as Jethro wove his way through the crowds of merrymakers back to his wife and family. He noted with pleasure the look of amazement as Jethro broke the news, and he raised his hat in acknowledgement as Mrs Parker looked across to where he stood, her hand to her mouth and tears in her eyes. He watched as she called her children, and broke the news that the family would after all be staying in Hensford, and pointed to their new home, the Lock-Keeper's cottage, not a stone's throw from where they now were. And then the excitement as William was told of his forthcoming trip to the famous Barnet Fair, 'over the hills, and far away.' And with that, Mr Clarke summoned his own wife, sons, and daughter, and guided them to their waiting carriage, leaving the village and its people to celebrate in their own festive manner as simple country folk had done since time immemorial.

Chapter Eight

Later That Evening
High Trees House

It was going to be the grandest gathering and the biggest party the valley had ever seen. Mr Clarke had given explicit orders that no expense was to be spared, and that all his business associates, from the valley and beyond, were to be invited to celebrate the end of a grand project and the start of a new life for them all. Invited were the 'great and the good' without whom the canal could not have been built, and Edmund's dream of linking Clarke's Quarry to London would have remained just that; a dream. The list included wealthy landowners, merchants, clergymen, and lawyers, not to mention bankers, barge-builders and industrialists, all whom stood to make small fortunes if the canal became the success they all envisaged. At the same time, no-one was fool enough to believe that this success was guaranteed, and all knew that many a fortune had been lost, as well as made, in the brave new world of canal transport. And as they climbed the hill in anticipation of their meal many said a silent prayer that their faith in Mr Clarke and his vision would be repaid, and that their money was safely invested in a man who knew exactly what he was doing...

*

An army of servants had been hard at work throughout the days leading up to the festivities, preparing High Trees for the occasion. Saunders stood, like a ringmaster in a circus, directing, cajoling, ordering and scolding his team of boys and girls, men and women, in the enormous task confronting them. Mrs Clarke, too, busied herself with overseeing Saunders in his tasks, and more than once she had ordered the complete re-decoration of the grand hall and changed her mind several times as to the colour scheme she desired.

In the kitchen, Mrs Drabble, the Cook, rolled up her sleeves and rallied the kitchen maids, the scullery maids, the roasting cook, and the baker to 'work harder, stop slouchin' and watch you're not standin' around if her ladyship turns up!' Everywhere, girls and women in bonnets and white aprons were running hither and thither while men and boys in waistcoats, their sleeves rolled up to their elbows, were making themselves busy lifting and carrying, cutting and basting, mixing and stirring. Every so often someone would stop to wipe their brow only to be scolded by the formidable Mrs Drabble, determined that the banquet would be 'fit for Good King George 'imself, if 'e were to turn up!' and then would return to their work with a grumble muttered quietly into their chests.

When bored, Adam, sixteen year-old heir to the estate, would sometimes venture downstairs to make his presence known. Any chat between the staff stopped immediately as workers focused hard on the task in-hand. Avoiding his cold gaze, they did their best to stay out of his way, afraid of attracting unwanted attention and the inevitable cutting remark. Adam, unaffected by their clear mistrust, would wander amongst them glorying in the power he possessed over these people, many old enough to be his father, or grandfather even. Little did he care for them or their sorry little lives –indeed he had no interest in them beyond their role in serving him and his kind. On one occasion a pan of boiling potatoes landed with a crash onto the tiled floor only for Adam to accuse Maisy, a timid scullery maid, of being a clumsy oaf. Embarrassed and upset she had run sobbing to the room she shared with three others. But Tom, the porter's assistant and Maisy's secret admirer, had seen it all, and later told her that it had been *Adam* who had knocked the pan to the floor in a deliberate effort to upset and humiliate her. Tension was running high and it amused Adam to see the servants scurrying like rats in their efforts to please their lord and master, his family, and their friends.

Any party at the house was a grand affair but this occasion was to be was grander than any that had gone before. At six o'clock precisely, the great front door was opened and the first of a hundred guests ascended the stairs, each to be welcomed with a loud announcement by Saunders: 'Mr and Mrs William Wiseman of The Chenies Estate; Lord and Lady Hoskins; The Duke and Duchess of Rutland...' As each arrived and was escorted to the banqueting room, Saunders would bow graciously and whisper his own personal welcome.

By the time the ornate clock at the foot of the staircase chimed six-thirty, all the guests were assembled and waiting to be seated, and fifteen minutes later, as the clock struck the quarter, the meal was underway and the conversation flowing. The dining room was resplendent with seasonal flowers, exotic ferns and palms, and in the centre of the tables bowls of red roses added yet more colour to the already splendid scene. At one end of room, on a gallery high above the guests, a small band played a selection of popular tunes much to the delight of both the visitors and the members of the High Trees staff who, when out of sight, would hum along to their favourites.

The meal itself was one that would stay in the memories of those present for months to come: pike and sole, boiled beef and ham, green roasted goose, turkey, rabbit, and duck, custard, tarts, jellies, strawberries, cherries, raisins and many more fruits -all washed down with copious amounts of wine, porter, and, of course, champagne.

Adam, whilst making sure that he had his fill of the delicacies on offer, looked with distain upon those who served him and took every opportunity to make his parents' servants remember their place. Purposely spilling the wine poured by a nervous waiter, for example, he rounded on him and shouted at him to 'return to the kitchens and stay there for the remainder of the evening!', an amusing episode perhaps to some of the snootier guests, but to Saunders standing nearby it appeared a needless act of spitefulness.

Otherwise, the evening proceeded wonderfully, with the ladies retreating to the drawing room, leaving their men to their after-dinner stories, cigars, and coffee, and ended well after midnight when all the guests finally left, and the mammoth job of clearing away the knives, forks, spoons, crockery and endless pieces of silver-plate could begin in earnest.

Wishing his wife goodnight, before falling into a deep, wine-induced sleep, Edmund Clarke, master of High Trees estate, reflected on what had been the perfect day to end to the best year of his life.

*

In another house, next to the lock, a little girl gripped her dolly ever more closely and dreamed that one day she might live in the big house at the top of the hill.

Chapter Nine

Early Morning September 3rd 1799
High Trees House

Jethro and William stopped at the ornate gates which marked the start of the long, winding drive leading to the home of Mr Clarke and family. It had been a long pull up the hill from the valley bottom, and both were a little breathless, their breathing made all the more difficult on account of the nervous excitement that both were feeling. It was still early morning and the sun peeped over the ridge of a distant hill, signalling the start of a two-day adventure that neither father nor son would ever forget.

'Can't stand here gawping all day m'boy,' said Jethro,' and, slapping his son on the shoulder, made his way towards the front of the grand house. William picked up his small bag, slung on the end of a short pole across his shoulder, and hurried after his father. His nerves were jangling and he wanted to be at Jethro's side at all times- at least until he felt more confident in these unfamiliar surroundings. As they made their way along the drive, the high trees of the house's name cast long blue shadows across their path. A pair of pheasants scuttled crazily out of the woods and into the adjacent field, and the bark of a fox was the only sound to disturb the early morning peace of this beautiful English late summer's day.

After what felt like an age, they stood together in front of the main doors of their master's house. Was it right to approach the front door as guests, or should they use the tradesmen's entrance hidden round the back? Both looked at each other anxiously before Jethro lifted his head confidently and stepped forward to lift and strike the large brass knocker three times firmly against the dark wood of the door. The knocks echoed back and forth across what was evidently a large empty space on the far side of the entrance. A minute-perhaps two-elapsed before footsteps confirmed the approach of somebody walking steadily to the other side of the door. It opened slowly, and there stood the imposing figure of Saunders, the footman who was to accompany the four of them on the journey to Barnet.

'Mister and Master Parker, I presume,' he said, and indicated that they should come in and take a seat. He noted, with a withering look down his alarmingly long nose, the dust on their boots and trousers and with a sigh turned and walked off to inform the Clarkes that their guests had arrived.

'I don't think he likes us dad,' whispered William nervously to his father. 'Didn't like the way he looked us up and down like we was worth nothing.'

Jethro hushed his son and told him to remember his place. Looking around, the walls of the entrance hall were more those of a church than a house. The Parkers had, quite literally, never seen anything like it. Large paintings depicted past generations of Clarkes, and one even showed the present Mr and Mrs Clarke with their three children. The family was painted standing beneath a tree-one of the 'high trees' no doubt- with what was recognisably the valley and the Chiltern Hills in the background. Edmund Clarke, resplendent in a fine white wig, stood proud and upright to the left whilst his wife sat upon a gold-red sofa to the right, dressed in her best blue silk gown and wide brimmed hat. The children surrounded their mother- a baby girl lay upon her lap whilst the elder of two boys stood at her side, the younger at her feet. All stared, confidently out of the picture towards some unseen distant horizon. This was a family of importance, it said, a family with a future.

Ten minutes passed before Edmund Clarke appeared at the top of the long double stairway. He walked briskly to the bottom before greeting his foreman and his son with hearty handshakes. 'Good to see you both, bright and early on this beautiful English morning! Chipping Barnet beckons Jethro, and we will be there by eveningtide! And you, young man, how does this day find you?'

William struggled to contain his nerves but managed to answer that he was very well and very much looking forward to his first visit to the famous Barnet Fair-one of the best in England, so he had heard.

'One of the best in *the world*!' young man, corrected the master of the house smiling, before slapping him on the shoulder and calling for his son, Adam, to meet their guests.

The boy made his way from a side room and joined them at his father's side. He was maybe two years older than William, taller, and dressed in clothes that mirrored those of his father: dark breeches tucked into knee length boots of supple leather, a simple waistcoat and silk neck-scarf, a long-tailed coat and a black tri-corn hat. Like the older man, he wore the short wig and pig-tail fashionable among the better classes. He looked the visitors up and down slowly and deliberately before reluctantly shaking hands. His was not the grip of a working man, thought William, and noted the paleness of the other boy's face and the softness of his skin.

'A pleasure to make your acquaintance,' said Adam with a weak smile before withdrawing his hand, wiping it covertly on his breeches, and taking two steps backwards.

'Have you breakfasted?' inquired Mr Clarke and was assured that they had, indeed, had enough to eat, Elizabeth having risen earlier than ever to prepare a breakfast of porridge and berries.

'That's grand,' said Mr Clarke, and suggested that with no more ado they make their way to the front of the house where Saunders and their carriage would be waiting.

The party, led by Mr Clarke, walked the short distance to the spacious area which fronted the house and overlooked the drive leading to the open road below. Mr Clarke's best carriage stood gleaming while Saunders and the driver did the final checks to the horses' tack and loaded the roof with the small amount of luggage needed for the trip. The leather cases of Mr Clarke and son stood in stark contrast to the simple bags of the Parkers, and in a few minutes all were secured, ready for departure. Saunders folded down the step to allow Mr Clarke and Jethro to enter the carriage, and then assisted the two boys to their seats. The two men faced each other across the space of the compartment, as did the boys, and the door was clicked shut. The carriage itself was comfortable if a little cramped for two men and their growing boys. William noted the seats of quilted leather and hardly knew where to rest his hands, such was the quality of the interior. Mr Clarke, noticing his discomfort, put him at his ease and informed him that he really should relax and enjoy the trip. He explained that the unusually wet August, followed by the present 'Indian Summer', had left the roads badly rutted and a little slow; but they were at least dry so that mud would not be a problem. Besides, he continued, the Clarkes' carriage was fitted with the latest in spring-iron suspension so that any bumps would be kept to a minimum. As he finished his sentence, Adam smiled and added pointedly that this was 'no mud-filled cart of the sort that the Parkers would be used to.' William looked at the floor and worried about the two days to come.

*

The following hours were spent looking at the passing countryside. Every now and again they would catch a glimpse of the Grand Junction Canal and the two men talked about the ease now with which goods would be transported from Hensford to the great city itself.

'As long as water falls from the sky and men live in houses this will be the way of the future, Jethro. Thousands of tons of chalk, and much else that the citizens of London will want or need, will be transported effortlessly along this glistening highway! No bumps or ruts on a canal mark you! Come rain or shine, smooth as a mill pond!' Mr Clarke enthused. At that precise moment the carriage was rocked by a particularly deep rut and Jethro smiled as he nodded in agreement with his employer. As the journey progressed, and the risen sun warmed the land, the four grew drowsy with Mr Clarke and then Jethro falling into fitful slumber. William and Adam sat, avoiding each other's gaze. The two boys did not talk and William was sure Adam stretched his legs deliberately long to cut down the space available to him. He chose to say nothing but felt deeply unhappy as the carriage rattled its way from village to village on its way to the celebrated market town of Chipping Barnet. How *was* he to survive two days in the close company of this boy who clearly loathed him and his father, and believed them to be unworthy to share even the smallest flake of their privileged existence?

Some two to three hours into their journey, the carriage rattled along a moorland road, straight and wide with views over the thickly wooded valley below. Here and there a few trees clustered together to break the monotony of the moor, and buzzards could be seen circling high overhead. As they approached a lonely cross roads Adam suddenly pointed excitedly ahead.

'Look! It's a gibbet! You can still see the skeleton inside! Slow down driver! Slow down!' he shouted.

William's gaze followed Adam's finger and he was repulsed by what he saw. Dangling from a wooden pole, fifteen feet above the ground, a metal cage, the size and shape of a man, twisted slowly to and fro in the breeze. Within the bars, the glistening white bones of a skeleton could clearly be seen together with the remains of whatever clothing the wretched creature had been wearing at the time of his execution. William looked away and said a silent prayer for the soul of the dead man.

'A better fate than he deserved, the scoundrel!' said Adam enthusiastically. 'Probably a highwayman or a cutpurse I'd wager. Let that be a lesson to them all –to all those who would take what is not theirs!'

William thought that he had never seen Adam look so animated; so happy, even.

'He probably needed to feed his starving family! We don't know *anything* about him except he was human, one of God's creatures!' he protested, then looked abashed as both older men turned their gaze on him.

It was his father who spoke. 'Will, it is in God's nature to be merciful, but those that steal and loot, and murder their fellow men will get their just desserts-both in this life and in the next. The Lord's Commandments must be kept even by the poorest and weakest in our midst. But may God have mercy on his soul!' And then he too bowed his head.

'May he rot in Hell as he did on earth!' spat Adam smiling, and craned his neck to catch a last glimpse of the cage as it gently creaked its mournful warning to all would-be criminals.

And it was then that William fully understood the gulf that separated his and Adam's life and knew for certain that they could never be anything but enemies.

*

The sun was hanging low in the western sky when Saunders announced that Chipping Barnet was just in sight. William leaned forward to look out of the carriage window and saw, between the trees, a weather-cock atop a distant church spire, glinting weakly in the fading light. How glad he would be to be rid of this carriage, a rattling prison cell from which there had been no escape since the break of day. How he longed for the fresh air and the chance to stretch his legs, and to put a decent distance between him and Adam with his cruel, mocking grin. As the carriage neared the town so the number of country-people heading the same way increased and the air grew thick with their cries and the sound of their animals. Young boys brandished long thin sticks as they ran, desperately attempting to steer gaggles of geese, loudly complaining, in the direction of market. And heavy Welsh Black cattle wandered ponderously from side to side, their huge heads twitching as swarms of gnats plagued their ears and eyes, and their drovers cursed and yelled in a language William recognised not. Elsewhere, tents and stalls were being erected, with traders loudly advertising their wares to anyone who passed by- live geese, shoes and bags of finest leather, herbs and potions, pots and pans, ropes, buckles, belts and beer....anything and everything an honest man or woman could possibly desire. William sat mesmerised, and Jethro smiled to see his son gape, wide-eyed, at the scene unfolding before them. Adam, by contrast, rolled his eyes and held a silk handkerchief tightly to his nose, making his disgust clear for all to see. This was not his first time at The Fair and his determination to spoil the visit for their guests was only too obvious to both William and his father. Mr Clarke, by contrast, seemed not to notice his son's behaviour.

The carriage slowed down to no more than a slow walking pace as the road became ever more rutted and almost impassable. Large pot-holes caused the carriage to rock alarmingly from side to side and an untidy mass of animals, their owners, and cursing market traders, threatened to block their way completely.

As they made their way deeper into the bustling town, Mr Clarke pointed out various buildings and places of interest- the ancient church with the spire they had seen some minutes earlier, the market cross, the square which would be the centrepiece of tomorrow's fair, and The Mitre Inn where the four of them would spend the night.

'Finest inn for many a long mile Jethro! Nothing but the best for Edmund Clarke and his associates!' And with that, he tipped his hat to an ageing servant who raised a gloved hand and greeted him with a hearty 'Wonderful evening, Mr Clarke!' The carriage trundled through the gateway, along a covered passage and into the courtyard beyond. Although busy, the yard was far enough away from the main street to seem quiet by comparison. Servants in their smart blue uniforms ran here and there carrying bags, doubling back to pick up fallen packages off the dusty ground, taking orders, giving orders and, at all costs, keeping busy -it would not do to be seen slacking. Not when the fair was in town!

The carriage finally creaked to a halt and the sound of stamping hooves could be heard from where the travellers sat and stretched, with William being careful to avoid the boots of his boss and those of Adam.

A younger servant, also dressed in blue and wearing a short white wig, opened the door and let down the steps of the carriage. First to emerge was Mr Clarke, followed by his son and then their guests. The servant offered a steadying hand to Mr Clarke who accepted with a nod, whilst Adam batted away the gloved hand as he would an irritating wasp or fly.

The four were shown to their rooms by the inn-keeper, a Mr Benjamin Smollett, who greeted Mr Clarke and son as old friends and valued customers. Asking after their health he assured them that he had reserved only the best rooms for Edmund and Adam and that their companions, the Parkers, would not be disappointed with their accommodation, either.

On parting, Mr Clarke instructed his guests that they should unpack their things, rest a short while, then join him and Adam downstairs for something to eat.

'Shall we say eight of the clock?' he suggested, to which Jethro agreed, then followed the manservant to the room that he and William had been allocated overlooking the main street at the front of the building.

*

The enticing smell of roasting beef told William and Jethro that the meal they had been long waiting for was almost upon them. Having washed their faces and changed into fresh shirts they made their way down the narrow staircase to the hallway where they had last seen their fellow travellers and had been made welcome by the innkeeper. Jethro straightened his son's collar before they entered the dining room where the Clarkes would be waiting. A crowd of perhaps twenty men stood around, tankards of ale in their hands, laughing loudly, swapping stories and generally getting into the spirit of the fair which came but twice a year.

'Jethro and young William! Come in, come in!' Mr Clarke had evidently been drinking for some time, his face flushed and his eyes slightly glazed from the beer he had already consumed.

'Everyone!' he shouted over the din of the conversations. 'Everyone, this is my good friend Jethro Parker and his eldest son William! Master canal diggers both, and Jethro now the esteemed lock-keeper of the best, the grandest, some might say..,' he searched hopelessly for an appropriate adjective, '... the *wettest* new canal in the whole of England. I give you The Parkers!' And with that he shook both vigorously by the hand and swiftly finished whatever was left of the drink in his tankard. A pot-boy, no more than ten years old, appeared suddenly and re-filled it with ale, spilling some onto the stone floor as he did so. Mr Clarke eyed the spillage blearily, swayed a little, belched, then bellowed an order for two more tankards of ale to be filled immediately for his guests.

'Eat, drink, and be merry!' he said much too loudly to the pair who, unused to the company, appeared somewhat embarrassed by the attention now being heaped upon them.

'To the glory of The Hensford Canal and the continuing success of Clarke's Quarry!' someone nearby cheered, and all present , including the Parkers, raised their tankards and drank deeply of the warm, dark brown liquid they contained. Someone else shouted 'God Save the King!', in response to which the company roared their approval and drank yet another noisy toast.

William scanned the room for Adam, only to find him leaning against the panelled wall, silently standing apart from the crowd, watching him and Jethro intently. On catching his eye, Adam raised his tankard and gave William the coldest of thin smiles, in stark contrast to Mr Clarke who was once again clapping him and his father about the shoulders and talking of his pride in the canal and his hopes for the future prosperity of the valley.

And so the evening progressed until, on the stroke of nine, a hatch clattered open and a series of dishes appeared, to be brought over by menservants and serving maids to where the diners sat around a long oak table. William and his father had never, in all their lives, seen such a feast.

To boisterous applause dish after dish was brought before them: beef (roast and boiled), legs of mutton, duck, partridge and rabbit. Bowls of cabbage, peas, potatoes, turnips and some vegetables which neither William nor his father had ever seen before, let alone eaten. And the plates! They were of the finest Wedgewood china-what would his mother have given for just one of these, he wondered. Not to be eaten off, but to be put in pride of place on the shelf above the fire, for all to admire.

The Parkers were quite accustomed to the rough manners of village folk, especially when there was ample good food to be eaten and the ale was flowing freely. The celebration of the canal opening itself was a fine example of this: a night not to be forgotten, but one that many who had been there could not in truth remember. Nevertheless, they were truly unprepared for the manners of the group of men with whom they had been invited to dine. Behaving no better than common roustabouts, food and drink, fit for a king, was spilt and thrown, wasted, with no thought for those who had prepared it or brought it to the table. Several times, friends of Adam left the room to be sick in order that they could return and gorge themselves again on the food and drink provided for them by Edmund Clarke. The host himself was by this time far too gone and 'in his cups' to notice and even less to care. William thought of his own family at home, and those of his fellow canal workers, and how they could live for a week on what these people threw on the floor or left for the dogs. They were *animals*, he thought angrily, but quickly corrected himself as he acknowledged the fact that animals behaved better in every way and certainly would not have treated food in such a disrespectful and wasteful manner.

As the evening wore on, the assembled friends and associates of the Clarkes grew louder and louder. Their conversation grew courser and their singing, tuneless even at the start of the meal, became steadily worse. Adam, William noticed, took every opportunity to make him feel that he should not be there, and that he was not worthy of being part of this, the Clarkes' annual pilgrimage to Barnet and its fair. Nods, winks, and knowing-looks between Adam and his friends, followed closely by mocking laughter, told him as much, and by the time the church clock struck eleven William was more than ready to take his leave and get to bed. Explaining that he was very tired from the journey, he thanked a very drunk Mr Clarke for his hospitality and made towards the door. His father had whispered to him that he would, indeed, follow shortly but that it would not be seen as good manners for both of them to leave at the same time. As William left, and coming from the corner occupied by Adam and his friends, he was sure he heard a familiar voice wishing him 'Sweet Dreams!' closely followed by a loud guffaw and the thumping of fists on the heavy table.

William kept his eyes forward, climbed the stairs wearily, and was fast asleep by the time his father bade his boss good-night, just half an hour later.

Chapter Ten

September 4th 1799
The Mitre Inn - Barnet

The next morning, William and his father woke early. The weak September sun leaked past the thin curtains of their room and a chill in the air hinted at the end of long summer days. Both had slept unusually well, their long day's travel and comfortable beds combining perfectly to guarantee a deeply satisfying slumber; and this despite the faraway sounds of shouting and raucous singing which had continued well into the small hours.

Following a hearty breakfast, at which Adam had said and eaten very little, the four assembled by the front entrance ready for their day at the fair. William, although clearly uncomfortable in the presence of his boss's son, admitted to being very excited at his first visit to what was universally recognised as the most famous fair in the land, and he looked forward eagerly to the sights and sounds of the day ahead.

The Mitre was a-buzz with activity and the streets around filled with growing crowds, and the sounds and stench of farm animals come to town was everywhere. This immediately made William feel at home again and he breathed in deeply, comforted by the lowing, the bleating and the snorting, enjoying the familiar smells. Adam, in contrast, clutched his handkerchief ever more tightly to his nose and looked disdainfully at the drovers and their like going about their business.

Edmund Clarke shared none of his son's sensibilities as he stood, hands on hips, chest thrust out, admiring the unfolding scene.

'Twenty thousand people a day, Jethro. Twenty thousand people from every corner of England-and Scotland, and Wales mind you- descend on this little market town! Can you imagine! For three days, each September, Barnet becomes the centre of God's universe! Whatever sight you can envisage, whatever amusement or distraction, whatever form of trade - good or bad-you can think of under the heavens, you will find it here! But have your wits about you because mixed in with the innocent beasts of the fields are rogues who would have your purse as soon as look at you. They'd sell their very mothers for an easy penny!' He shook his head and laughed to himself before adding, 'but let's not be of faint heart my friends, let us go and enjoy the spectacle that is Barnet Fair!' And with that, he strode into the street known as Middle Row, under the shadow of the tower of St John the Baptist's church, and led his guests along Wood Street with its fine houses and roughly- erected market stalls.

The rest of the day was spent wandering the streets and alleyways that made up the fair. Animals were everywhere and you had to be careful where you stepped to avoid finding yourself lying on your back, the butt of jokes for all who saw you slip. Adam made his way gingerly along the filthy streets, carefully avoiding whatever the animals had chosen to leave behind, avoiding too any contact with their rough-looking owners. Meanwhile, William observed the business of the market and marvelled at the bartering and the vast amounts of money changing hands.

Every so often Mr Clarke would take him or his father by the elbow and quietly point out a young boy standing, to William's inexperienced eye, quite innocently, watching the buying and selling of a bull or a pair of horses. Standing behind a country gent, the boy would dip his hand stealthily into the rich man's pocket, and in a flash would be away, a silk handkerchief or even a gold watch firmly in his grasp. Disappearing into the confusion, the cries of 'Cutpurse! Thief!' would be ringing in his ears.

'Be aware! Very aware!' said Mr Clarke wryly. 'They'll take the very shirt off your back!'

But the fair was not all about the sale of animals and Mr Clarke was keen to show his guests the full range of amusements and distractions for their entertainment and delight. At one point, one of the many gypsies to be found selling their wares and plying their traditional trades tugged William's sleeve gently and asked, in a strong country accent, if 'the young gentleman would wish to 'ave his fortune told?' Mr Clarke, enjoying the moment, dug out a silver coin from his own pocket and gave it to the old lady who studied it briefly before pocketing it herself and taking William's hand in her own. Bending his fingers back gently, she ran a bony digit over his workman's palm, looking intently at the lines and what their story told. She said he was a hard-working boy and one with great faith. She squinted with ageing eyes and revealed, much to the group's amazement, how he had 'a way with 'orses beyond the ordinary. You speak their language and they understand, young sir!' she said, and a bashful William confirmed that this was indeed the case. But then her toothless smile disappeared and she turned away, folding his fingers back into a fist, before declaring his session finished and that he should go now and not return. A look of fear was in her eyes as she disappeared into the makeshift tent that was her home for the day. William made to ask her the meaning of her discomfort but was led away by Mr Clarke who chortled that it was all 'stuff and nonsense, and old wives' tales.' Adam, who had witnessed the exchange, stood aside and smirked slyly to himself, evidently feeling all the better for William's discomfort.

A little later, they found themselves in a corner of the fair dominated by tradesmen and women selling clothes and hats of all descriptions-from the simple and rustic, to the fine, expensive silks worn only by the well-to-do. Cobblers thrust their boots of soft leather at the four as they moved through the crowds and a group of young girls caused the boys to blush as they held up shirts and breeches declaring them to be 'just the thing for 'ansome young gents, such as yerselfs'. But one item did take William's eye, and no amount of pretending could disguise his interest. It was a soft leather hat, brown, with a wide rim, and a bright red band circling its crown. There was something distinctive-distinguished almost- about it and William handled it fondly before trying it on at the insistence of the old man running the stall.

'It could have been made 'specially for you, young sir!' declared the man. 'Makes you look quite the true gent! The lasses will swoon at the very sight! And all for a mere guinea- cheap at twice the price!'

William laughed and admired himself in the chipped looking-glass held up by the hat-seller. 'What do you think dad?' he asked, and his father agreed that he did in-fact look quite the gent, but a guinea is a guinea and he already had a perfectly good hat at home...

William took off the hat slowly and handed it back to the seller, the look of disappointment clear for all to see.

'Nonsense, Jethro! I will not hear of it!' cried Mr Clarke, again digging his hand into his pocket ,and slapping a coin firmly into the stall-holder's hand, before taking the hat back and thrusting it onto the young man's head.

'I'll brook no argument, mind!' he said, as both William and his father started to object weakly, and then followed him as he walked briskly away and into the crowd once more.

Proudly wearing his new hat, William imagined that all eyes were upon him as he and his father enjoyed the sights and sounds of the fair. They watched open-mouthed as local lads attempted to climb the greasy pole, only to fall with a thump on the dusty ground, all to the evident amusement of onlookers who smiled and shook their heads at the foolishness of youth. Elsewhere, older men and women grinned and gurned at passers-by, their toothless heads and lolling tongues framed by huge, leather horse collars; small children hunted a pig with a soapy tail, the animal squealing its displeasure as it darted between legs in a frantic effort to escape their grasping hands, and a giant of a man walked through the crowds holding a wooden beer barrel high above his head, as if it were a feather.

As night began to fall, the crowd gradually dispersed and made for the ale-houses and inns of which there were many. Mr Clarke suggested that they too should return to The Mitre where he was sure the Parkers would enjoy what was left of their day. Both Jethro and William were tired and looked forward to a brief rest on their comfortable beds before joining the Clarkes for dinner. Adam had made very little conversation with any of the group during the day and maintained his distance as they walked, and talked, their way back to the inn.

The evening meal followed a similar pattern to the previous evening. Mr Clarke was again, of course, the centre of attention, well-known to locals and annual visitors alike. The wine and the ale again flowed freely and the smoke-filled rooms were alive with much eating, laughter and, as the evening progressed, more tuneless singing. William and his father joined in as best they could but could not disguise their distaste at the behaviour of some of the others present. Adam showed no such discomfort and joined in heartily, the food and drink spilling down his front as he swayed around the room, rudely grabbing the serving girls around their waists whilst trying to catch an unwanted kiss. He remained just sober enough to note, with a bleary-eyed contempt, the Parkers as they bade an early good night to his father and made their way up-stairs to bed. For the Parkers it was a disappointing end to what had been an eventful day but William, much to his father's amusement, lifted their mood by insisting on wearing his fine new hat to bed just as his sister always slept cuddling her dolly.

Jethro snuffed out the candle and spoke to the darkness. 'Well my boy, I am pleased that you enjoyed the day and that you now have a fine nightcap to go with your nightshirt! I was proud of you today Will, which, I fear, is more than Mr Clarke will be able say of *his* son.'

And without further elaboration, he asked God to protect them both, closed his eyes, and fell into a deep sleep.

*

A crowing cockerel woke William early and he drew the blankets a little closer around his shoulders, then rolled to face the wall.

'William, are you awake?' It was his father whispering through the gloom of their wood-panelled room. 'We need to rise and make ready to leave within the hour. Are you awake, my boy?'

'Aye, father, I am,' said William and pulled the rim of the hat he still wore over his eyes. 'How was I to sleep with the noise of this place going on all night? No sooner do I fall asleep and you are telling me it's time to wake up! Oh, how I now long for my own bed, small and hard as it is.'

'Enough of that William!' scolded his father. 'Mr Clarke and Adam, in their generosity, have provided for us handsomely this past two days. We need to show our appreciation. And remember this Will, it is only because of Edmund Clarke's kindness that we still *have* our own beds and a roof over our heads in Hensford. Don't forget that son, and don't forget your place!'

William grumbled his agreement and swung his legs onto the floor, shivering a little as the coolness of the early morning air shocked him into life once more. He pulled back the thin curtain, allowing a shaft of light to illuminate the bed on which his father was now sitting up. It was too early for more chat and both of them dressed and washed their faces in the cold water from a rough basin on the one small sideboard. It was going to be another long day and they needed to take breakfast and be ready without delay.

Ten minutes later, they were making their way down the narrow staircase and entering the room where breakfast was to be served.

Mr Clarke, bleary eyed from the night before, acknowledged their entrance with a small wave of his hand and a hoarse 'Morning, Jethro', whilst Adam refused to look up from where he sat. William thought the boy looked ill, the scant colour he once had having totally drained away, leaving his face even more deathly white, and silent. 'Damn well serves you right, Adam!' William thought to himself, and counted this as another little victory in their private war; a war which William himself had not chosen to be a part of, but from which he was unable to escape as long as the Clarkes owned the canal and the Parkers 'knew their place', and did as they were expected...

Chapter Eleven

September 5th 1799
The Clarkes' Carriage

From far behind, the travellers heard the church bell strike nine as they settled down for the journey ahead of them. The open fields were slowly making way for woodland, thin and patchy at first, denser and darker the further into the forest they travelled. As on the way in, Mr Clarke fell into a shallow sleep whilst Jethro shut his eyes and thought about Alice and his other children, by this time up from bed and making themselves busy around the house. Even, perhaps, preparing for a day's work at the plaiters' school. William rested his head on the leather of the carriage side and looked out of the open window; Adam stared stonily ahead, sickness in his eyes and on his cheeks. The rhythm of the hooves on the hard ground and the movement of the carriage had an almost hypnotic effect and, despite the frequent ruts in the highway, William also struggled to stay awake. Boredom set in and those still awake looked forward to nothing more than the canal and the familiar sights of Hensford and its peaceful valley.

As they travelled further into the forest, they started a long ascent of one of the many chalk hills that lay between the market town of Barnet and the village of Hensford. The horses struggled to keep up the pace and the driver was forced on many occasions to crack the whip. Unseen amongst the trees ahead, two pairs of eyes picked out the shape of the approaching carriage, and without a word masks were adjusted and tri-corn hats pressed firmly into position. One of the men nodded and their horses were spurred viciously into action.

Suddenly, and without warning, the carriage swerved and swayed viciously from side to side. Men's voices could be heard shouting angrily over the sounds of the startled horses and the furious rattling of the wheels. The carriage shuddered to an untidy stop throwing the two adults forward to join their sons in a heap on the front bench. Mr Clarke, awake in a flash, pushed his face towards the window only to be met by another face, masked and sinister, thrusting into the compartment from the outside.

'Stand and Deliver!' screamed the mouth hidden beneath the mask, causing the red material to move in and out violently in time with the words. 'Your money, or your life!'

'My God! Highwaymen!' said Mr Clarke as he fell backwards into his seat. 'Don't move or they'll kill us all!'

The man on the horse wrenched open the small door to reveal two pistols, cocked and ready to fire, pointing directly at the four terrified travellers. As Mr Clarke gasped for breath and put his hand to his throat, Adam fell to the floor and rolled himself into a ball as if by doing so he would become invisible to the masked robber and his demands.

Outside, a second voice, shriller and more nervous than the first, thought William, could be heard warning the coachmen not to try anything foolish. Above the beating of his heart and the neighing of the terrified horses he thought he heard Saunders saying something about having nothing of value on board- begging them to spare their lives.

The man at the door shouted again, pointing his guns first at Mr Clarke and then at each of the others in turn.

'Give me your money, damn you, or I'll be forced to let my friends here do the talking,' he demanded, a more desperate edge now to his voice.

'I swear,' implored Mr Clarke, 'we have little of value to give. We came only to enjoy the fair at Barnet and are returning home empty handed!'

On the floor Adam was whimpering quietly as he attempted to crawl beneath the feet of Jethro and William. 'Tell him to go father. Please! Make him go away!' he whined.

This seemed to enrage the man in the mask even further.

'That's right Mister! Make me go away-now! Hand over your money or, by God, you and your pox-ridden son will not see another day!'

'For the love of God!' said Edmund Clarke quietly, his voice revealing the hopelessness with which he viewed the situation, 'I swear, we have nothing to give you!'

The highwayman struggled to keep his horse in check as the other animals continued to panic, wide eyed, amidst the commotion. He levelled his gun once more at Mr Clarke and was issuing a last warning when he was interrupted mid-sentence. 'John! John!' a panicked voice caused him to look anxiously over his shoulder. 'It's the Post-Coach! I can hear its horn a-blowing! Let's be off! *Now!* Before it's too late!'

Sure enough, William could hear the faint sound of a distant horn which signalled the approach of the carriage, with its well-armed guard, carrying the mail towards Barnet and onwards to London.

But 'John' (if this indeed was his real name) was not to be denied his reward so easily.

At the exact moment that he straightened his arm in readiness to fire at Mr Clarke, William's voice cut through the chaos.

'Here, John, take this!' he said, and thrust a small purse, pulled from beneath his leather waistcoat, towards the villain. 'Take it! Take it! It is all I possess! But take it and be off while you still have time! The Post-coach approaches apace! Be off!'

The man grabbed the purse, loosened its top, and peered inside. Gold sovereigns were what he desired, and here they were- eight, nine, ten? Enough to keep them comfortable until the next carriage passed their way. The shrill 'halloo' of the approaching post-coach was getting louder, and his companion shouted ever more anxiously at him to leave the carriage to its journey before it was too late. Death by hanging-and then the gibbet- was what a highway robber could expect, and he was not ready yet to meet his maker.

With a whoop, the robbers dug their heels cruelly into the sides of their horses and spun away into the blackness of the forest, their cloaks streaming behind. The dust from the thundering hooves hung in the air and was just beginning to settle when the post-coach rounded the bend and came to its own juddering halt.

Mr Clarke slumped back in his seat, a look of stunned amazement upon his face. Jethro, head bowed, was mumbling a quiet prayer of thanks for their safe delivery from danger, while Adam snivelled and moaned upon the carriage floor. William it was who remained composed and leant over to touch his father's hand reassuring him that all was now well and that God had seen fit to protect the travellers so they could live to see another day.

Some moments passed before Mr Clarke could speak.

'Young William, we owe this day our lives to you! I thank you from the bottom of my heart! Without you we would surely today have entered the gates of Heaven! Jethro, you have a fine son, the bravest of boys!'

Jethro looked over to his son and joined him on the seat vacated by Adam who was by then beginning to unfold himself in to a sitting position on the dusty floor of the carriage.

Hugging his son, he kissed him on both cheeks, telling him he was indeed the bravest of the brave-a man amongst men! He told him how proud he was, and how proud the whole village of Hensford would be on learning of his bravery in saving Mr Clarke and all of them from violent deaths at the hands of a bloodthirsty and murderous pair.

But suddenly, a puzzling thought struck him, and he pulled back confounded to look his son full in the face.

'Will,' he quizzed his son, 'from where on God's earth did you get the money-the purse of money that you gave to the robber?' Mr Clarke also sat up and, now he had had time to compose himself, leant forward, intrigued to know where the boy could have acquired such a sum of money. 'A Parker?' he thought, 'with a purse of sovereigns enough to satisfy a money-grabbing rogue-it was just not possible!'

'Bad Money dad-not the real stuff,' William explained almost shyly. 'I had heard that this dark forest was a place where highwaymen prey upon travellers such as ourselves. I was afraid and found a man who could provide a purse of bad money at a price that I could afford. I thought it would be safest. You are not angry with me I hope?'

'Angry? How could I be *angry* with you when you have saved our lives?' And with that, he hugged his son closer still while Mr Clarke patted his shoulder firmly in thanks.

Meanwhile, Adam was now sitting upright and looking at William through new eyes. Where once he disliked the boy- he now despised him.

*

The remainder of the journey passed without incident. How could anything happen to compare with what had occurred earlier that day? Still in shock, nobody slept and few words were spoken. Adam, once the post-coach had checked that all were well and had gone on its way, got off the carriage floor, but now sat next to his father, not bearing to sit near this 'hero' of a boy.

On arrival at the High Trees, Jethro and William thanked Mr Clarke for his kindness and said goodbye to Adam who acknowledged their words with a surly nod of the head. Mr Clarke thanked them in turn for their good company and once again praised William for his brave deed which had saved them all from a cruel fate. At this, Adam turned on his heel and without a word moved away and stood some way off, his displeasure being clear for all to see. He addressed Saunders rudely who, bowing dutifully, obeyed his barked order to remove his leather bags to his room, 'Now! And without delay!'

Walking slowly down the long drive, the Parkers were sure they heard the raised voices of Mr Clarke and his son arguing as they made their way from the dusty carriage and into the safety of their beautiful house.

Chapter Twelve

Wednesday October 6th 2010
The Fairway - Hensford

The five of them formed an unlikely crew as they made their way from school to the canal museum. The boys, firmly anchoring the two ends of the line, the teacher positioned at number two, and a pair of girls, arms linked, chatting as they went. David tried to remain optimistic despite the obvious frostiness between Lee and Alex and was, quite frankly, amazed at how well the two girls seemed to be getting on. He'd already performed the miracle of actually getting the project off the ground and had received Ted's blessing-literally, in fact, with Ted dubbing him on each shoulder using a metre –rule he kept in his office for occasions just such as this. Ted could be strange at times, but he obviously enjoyed his job. Getting these particular four youngsters together had also been not without its challenges. When David announced the names of the lucky four chosen to help him with his local history project, there had been an audible gasp of disbelief in class, and he had had to keep his fingers tightly crossed behind his back when he swore that the draw had been fair and honest, Mr Richards pulling out the names in front of two other members of staff, the identities of whom he claimed to have forgotten. The girls were fine about it, Alex was keen, as he liked history, but Lee had taken some convincing, finally giving way when he realised that it meant several afternoons away from the classroom to visit one of the places he loved best in the world: the canal.

'Right, stop there, by the pub carpark, and we'll cross as a group.'

For a small place the traffic through the village could be horrendous and David wanted to do things absolutely by the book. The four children stopped as requested, each one looking down at their feet. Without warning, Lee burst out laughing, quickly followed by Alex. The boys looked firmly at the ground; the girls just rolled their eyes.

'What is it lads?' asked David, looking around for clues. 'What's the joke?'

'It's nothing,' Lee attempted to say, choking on his words and unable to meet David's stare. Alex too almost doubled over before Jo explained.

'It's the pub, sir. The Cock Inn. They think it's really funny.'

'Ugh, gross,' said Kirsty, curling her lip while also desperately trying to supress a smile herself.

'Oh, for goodness sake boys!' said David, in his best stern-teacher voice, before turning to face the other way and allowing himself a fleeting, schoolboy snigger.

'Right, let's cross-now!' he said, and all crossed quickly to the safety of the far pavement.

The last few hundred yards were through back lanes which Lee promised would bring them out on the canal, just along from the lock and the museum. The two girls resumed their conversation, reflecting on the childishness of the boys- well *boys*- agreeing that the village split was something they, the girls, could not be bothered about really.

'My mum says they've got too much testerone and as far as I'm concerned they can keep it,' said Kirsty, to which Jo agreed, saying that she didn't care about where people lived and that some of Lee's friends were actually quite fanciable.

David, meanwhile, was mentally preparing his introduction to Mrs Huggins, the museum curator, quietly pleased that the boys were sharing a laugh at least, albeit at his expense.

*

They arrived at the museum at just after one-thirty. David reminded the four of them to remember their manners and to ask questions if they didn't understand anything, then pushed at the door and walked in. Just as he remembered it, the room they entered was more like a shop than a museum, but all around the far wall, and out of sight of the window, were photographs, etchings, and prints, all of which appeared to recall Hensford's past. And down below, under the bottom shelf of a display unit, they could see grey cardboard storage boxes, plain but for the white sticky labels, now collecting what was evidently the most recent of many layer of dust. It was a dark place, gloomy and unlit.

The tinkle of the door- bell had alerted someone in the backroom and they were suddenly aware of the sound of that person stirring, getting up from a chair perhaps, and coming closer.

'Coming! Sorry, post-prandial nap...I'm on my way!'

The beaded curtain parted, and an oldish lady emerged, half-moon spectacles dangling from a gold-coloured chain around her neck.

David stepped forward and offered his hand. 'Mrs Huggins, I presume.'

'You presume right; and you must be Mr Stacey!' They shook hands, and David indicated the four youngsters standing beside him.

'And you must be Lee, you Alex, you Kirsty, and *you* must be Jo.' She pointed to each in turn.

'Well,' said Jo, 'I'm Jo and she's Kirsty, but otherwise you got it right Mrs Huggins. That's really good.'

'Dash it! Thought I'd hit the jackpot-but never mind, not bad for an old bird. And by the by, we'll drop the Mrs Huggins.

Such a stupid name. Call me Grandma Dot- everyone else does.'

'Are you sure, Mrs...?'

'Absolutely, Mr Stacey' she interrupted, 'and so what shall we call *you*?'

Four pairs of eyes looked at their teacher, anticipating his reply- Mr Stacey or David. What was it going to be?

'Well, Grandma Dot, I think it's got to be David to you, and,' he said turning towards his pupils, 'Mr Stacey or Sir to the kids.' He smiled and noticed their shoulders slump a tad, resigning themselves to the maintenance of the status quo.

'Drinks everyone? You must be parched after your walk- you've come from the High School haven't you? I'll have to disappear backstage again I'm afraid. Coke, Coke, Coke, Coke and tea all right?' And without waiting for an answer, she headed for the beaded curtain again. 'Make yourselves comfortable- won't be a minute.' It was only then that they noticed the floral leggings and Reebok trainers, the *must-have* and latest design, that the old lady was wearing below her comfortable grey cardigan.

David pointed to a low coffee table and dragged over enough chairs for them to sit around- a little more intimately than anyone might have wished, perhaps. A few minutes later, the old lady appeared pushing a small trolley bearing four cans of coke, a teapot with knitted cover, and a pair of china cups complete with matching saucers. A plate of bourbons and dairy creams caught the eye of Lee whose hand moved imperceptibly towards the lower shelf before he remembered where he was.

'Now then children, help yourselves to drinks and, David, I'll be mother if that's alright.' The four children helped themselves to a can of coke each and watched intently while Grandma Dot stirred the pot several times before pouring the tea through a strainer and handing David his cup, saucer and tea-spoon. This in itself was something akin to a Japanese Tea Ceremony to the youngsters and transported David, even, a few dozen miles to Muswell Hill and the week he'd spent with his mother and father in the summer.

'Not hungry? Don't like biscuits?' the old lady asked, breaking the spell, and Lee was able at last to take a bourbon, remembering, when elbowed by Kirtsy, to hand them around the table.

'Well! Welcome to The Adam's Lock Canal Museum! I'm *so* glad to see you- most of my visitors come from anywhere but Hensford- walkers and canal-boat owners mainly, on their way to somewhere else. And, and there's nothing wrong with this you understand,' she said, her voice dropping to a barely audible whisper, 'they're nearly all *old*!'

The children laughed and so did David.

'No, there's nothing wrong with getting older Grandma Dot,' he said. 'It comes to us all in time, but I'm really pleased too that you have made it possible for some of the younger ones- and from Hensford at that- to visit the museum.'

 A short silence descended as Grandma Dot beamed a little at her guests. Then Alex burped, causing the children to burst out laughing again and the old lady to reassure David that it really was alright, that we all do it, and that no harm was done.

'So, how is it I can help you?' she continued, pulling herself upright, establishing her position as the museum's curator.

'Who'd like to have a go at explaining our project?' asked David looking round. 'Jo, how about you?'

Jo mirrored the old lady's posture and smoothed her skirt before placing her hands palms down on her knees.

'Right, it's like this Mrs Hug, Grandma Dot,' she corrected herself. 'As part of PSHE –that's like a *getting to know yourself and other people* lesson- we are doing something about our local area- especially its history and all that. Mr Richards- he's our head of year- thinks we need to learn about Hensford and what happened in the past. We learn all about ancient Greeks and the Romans but he thinks we should know more about our own history. So, he asked Mr Stacey, *Sir,*' she said with an emphasis that really wasn't necessary, 'to bring some of us here; to see what we can find out.'

'Well,' David continued for her, 'that's ninety percent right Jo, but Mr Richards didn't ask me to come here specifically. I found out about the museum after chatting to someone else in the staffroom; but everything else you said was just about correct.'

'How thrilling!' Grandma Dot said. 'And *specifically*, is there anything you would like to know? Just so I can point you in the right direction; or at least try.'

'Alex. Can you add something here please?' said David, knowing this might be a little too difficult for Lee, maybe a step too far at this point in the proceedings.

Alex bristled a little and looked to the others for a level of assistance which was clearly not going to be forthcoming.

'Right, Grandma Dot,' he started, 'where to begin? Do you know about the problem between the Uppers and the Lowers?' he asked, starting with what he considered the most basic information required.

'Well, I'm not actually from the village but I am aware that, how shall we put it, 'tensions exist' between the different parts.'

'Oh good,' said Alex, keen to keep going if he could, 'so that's not a good thing really and we, that is Mr Richards, Mr Stacey and us, the class, sort of want to find out a bit about where the problem started and if there is anything we can do to make it better. You know, for us, for future generations, blah, blah, blah.'

'Sounds like a plan, doesn't it?' she replied looking around the table. 'Makes perfect sense to me, and I'll be happy to do what I can to help you in this quest,' she added with a pronounced nod. 'Nice word that, *quest*, don't you think?'

'That's brilliant Grandma Dot,' said David, relieved that things had got off to a good start. 'What do you say we make a start, once you've finished your drink and biscuits?'

*

It was two o'clock. The children and David had been ushered through to the backroom where Grandma Dot had set up a trestle table, and cleared a space for the five of them to start their research.

'Right. How about these for starters? They're a jumble of things really-old photographs, pictures, the odd bit of writing. Things we just haven't got room for on the walls. After all, this was designed to be an eighteenth century lock-keeper's cottage, and not a twenty-first century museum! If there's anything else you need, any more boxes you'd like to see, just let me know. I'll be next door making m'self useful.'

David thanked her and organised the boxes along the far edge of the table.

'Right. Off we jolly well go then, I suppose. How shall we go about this, then?' he asked the children.

'Us girls, we'll have a look at this box,' indicated Kirtsy, 'and the boys can start with the others. Is that alright?'

'Boys?' David looked at Alex and Lee, who shrugged their approval then opened the top of a large cardboard container, more of a crate really than a box.

'Great. And don't forget to share anything exciting you find. It would be nice to tell the rest of the class what we've discovered-might even do an assembly.'

'Sir!' Lee said, 'you didn't say anything about an assembly! I hate speaking in front of people!'

'Okay,' David reassured him. 'Just make a note of anything you find. Oh, and be careful- some of this stuff is really old and we need to make sure we don't damage it. I'm just going next door, see what's on the walls, maybe have a chat with Mrs Huggins; Grandma Dot, I mean.'

When David left the room the two boys looked at each other, unsure of who should do what, who should take the lead.

'D'you wanna go first?' said Lee, and took a small step back from the table.

'Okay. If you don't want to. You know, I don't mind.'

'Not bothered.'

Alex dipped his hands into the box and chose to remove a large wooden frame. As it emerged, he turned it over, face up, onto the table. The glass was dusty, but a quick wipe with his elbow revealed a photograph-sepia and white- two dozen faces staring out across the years.

'Looks like a wedding,' said Lee. 'Look, she's got a big bunch of flowers.'

Alex said nothing but leant a little closer, angling the picture better, avoiding the glare of the strip light which was bouncing back off the glass.

The group, some sitting, most standing, eyed the camera stiffly, the bride alone allowing herself the mere hint of a smile on this, *her* special day. The groom leant inwards towards his new wife lending, together with the linking of arms, a faintly proprietorial air to his gait. Surrounding the pair, and caught for eternity in the magnesium-flash of an early camera, their family and friends bore witness to this happy day, serious and formal, self-conscious and resolute. What struck Alex immediately were the clothes-and the inordinately large amount of male facial hair. A soldier standing just behind the groom looked for all the world like Kitchener, ready to announce that your country needs you. Three medals on his chest confirmed that he, at least, had done his bit. And then, there were the hats. Huge and circular they balanced precariously on the heads of every female apart from the bride, like something from a fancy dress party or a television drama of the sort his mum would watch. On the far left, and looking as if he didn't belong, sat the dark-suited figure of the reverend. His thin hand seemed to fiddle with a watch-chain…maybe he had other things to do: another wedding to perform perhaps, a recently-deceased member of his congregation to lower into the ground?

'Good, isn't it?' Alex looked up from the photograph.

'Yeah. It's good. Who's all the people?' Lee asked, and craned his neck to get a better look. 'Cor, look at that hat! It's like an extra-large pizza or something!'

They both laughed, and the girls asked them to explain themselves. Alex held the picture to his chest so they could see, and they dropped what they were doing and joined the boys.

'Oh, amazing clothes!' said Jo, touching the glass as if to feel the textures, to sense the softness of the feather boa, the stiffness of the bonnets.

'Must be hundreds of years old, at least,' said Lee, to be corrected by Alex who told him cameras weren't invented that long ago.

'Looks like something from the Victorians or something,' said Kirtsy, and everyone nodded their agreement.

'Found something interesting?' It was David, coming back into the room. 'Wow! That's brilliant!' he added, saying that he thought it probably *was* a late Victorian scene, the drooping handlebar moustaches and ornate headwear of the ladies being something of a give-away. 'What else have we got?'

The children resumed their search and David returned to the front room, allowing the four of them the space he felt they needed. He sat down and read some leaflets, chatted with Grandma Dot, and checked his e-mails. This, he thought, felt particularly odd in a place of such historic charm, built as it was at a time when electric lighting and the telegraph were still many years off.

Alex had made way for Lee as the contents of a second box started to pile up on their end of the table. More photos of the village high street, gas-lit and strewn with manure, mixed with more modern views of the same street: cars, motorbikes and mothers pushing prams, the garish colours dominating and somehow managing to diminish, rather than augment, the scenes.

Uncovering a mid-century photo entitled 'Canal Festival circa 1957', Lee was reminded of what his grandfather had told him. About his time as a boy, and how before they had stopped it, sometime in the 60's, the whole village had celebrated for a week, usually at the end of May, if his memory served him well. *'Great times, Lee'* his granddad has told him, *'but you had to be handy with your fists if you were still out on a Saturday night!'*

Last out of the box was a plain brown envelope, about A4 size. Lee carefully opened the flap then carelessly waved the envelope about until the photograph it contained slipped out and landed on the floor, face down. Turning it over, he was thrilled to recognise the unmistakable line-up of a football-team photograph.

'It's a footie team! Jeez, look at the shorts!' he said, almost to himself. 'Oh, I forgot. Not really your sport, is it Alex.'

'Well, if you must know, I do like football as well as rugger. Just not the thing to admit sometimes, is it? Not round here, anyhow.'

'What's your favourite team then?' asked Lee, somehow doubting Alex's claim.

'The Gunners. Who's yours?' said Alex.

'The same!' said Lee, reassured. 'It's a family tradition- goes back years.'

'Let's have a look then,' said Alex, and called the girls over to look at what they'd found. The four of them pored over the picture with Kirtsy recognising an old mill in the background, now converted into canal-side flats for the newly rich.

'He looks about fourteen and this one, he must be sixty!' Lee commented. Funny old team, half of them's kids and the other half's grandads.'

Jo put her nose to the picture, squinting at the faded sign held up by the players sitting in the centre. 'I think it says '*Hensford United A.F.C.*' she said slowly, 'and it says something like *Cup Winners 1916*. Yay, we won the cup!' The children all cheered bringing through both David and Grandma Dot to find out what the racket was about.

'Well, who would have believed it?' said the old lady, holding the picture at arms length and adjusting her glasses. 'Not only did we win the cup, but Hensford was *united* too! What date was it, Jo dear?'

'1916 is what it says.'

'Ah, right in the middle of the First World War - The Great War.'

'That'll explain why there are so many young and old players. All the others were away fighting,' said Alex.

'What, from *Hensford*?' asked Kirsty.

'Well, yeah,' said Lee. 'I mean the Germans didn't say 'Vee declare vore on Eng-er-land, but not on Hensford!' At least I don't think they did.'

'Quite right, Lee,' David allowed himself a laugh, 'and well done for all your detective work. What about you, girls?'

'A lot of pictures, and this old map. Says 1795 on it, and there's no canal but we found High Trees House, which we think is the High Trees Conference Centre or something now. It's in the right place.'

Lee broke in excitedly, 'That's where my mum works, she's a clea...she works in the office,' he corrected himself.

The clock on the wall chimed three signalling the end of their time at the museum- for today at least.

Chapter Thirteen

Wednesday October 13th 2010
Big Ted's Office

'And finally...' Big Ted pressed the down arrow on his laptop, 'we come to David and his local-history project. Over to you Mr Stacey.'

Half a dozen faces turned towards David.

'Right.'

'Oh, and don't be long. The Feathers is open,' Ted added, tapping his watch.

Miss McFadyen, head of RE, rolled her eyes then sat up straighter in her chair. She gave David a weary, knowing look.

'Right,' David continued, 'well, we finally managed to get ourselves down to the canal museum as planned.'

'We?' asked Mary, with a smile.

'Sorry Mary, that's me, Alex Clarke, Lee Parker, Jo Simmonds, and Kirsty...Kirsty...'

'Brown?' suggested a voice from the end of the table.

'That's her. So, we spent an afternoon with Mrs Huggins, the proprietor, looking through all sorts of stuff they managed to find. Mainly photographs, maps and things. It was the kids that did it; I sat next door and let them get on with it, really.'

'Nice work if you can get it, eh?' said Ted, before asking David to explain what the 'outcomes' of the day were. 'You know, I've got to record that in the minutes-justify my decision and all that.'

David took out his phone and searched for the photos he'd taken. 'Well, how about *this* one for the album then!'

He held up the image of four beaming children bending over a small picture of a football team, the two boys and two girls holding their arms aloft and appearing to cheer.

'Hensford United-Cup Winners-1916. Belated celebrations,' said David.

'Blimey Dave, that's nothing short of miraculous. The win *and* the kids I mean. Has young Clarke got his arm round Parker's shoulder? What do you think Mary- has your colleagues done enough for a beatification? Another Saint David, or *Dewi Sant* as we say in Wales. What would Father Murphy down at Our Lady's say, d'you think?'

'I really have no idea, Mr Richards, but I'm sure we should all join together in congratulating David here on a significant victory of a kind. Well done, Dave, keep battling on!' she said, smiling.

'Right,' said the year head, crestfallen by the teacher's reluctance to join in with his harmless conceit.

'Okay Dave, what shall I put? Something like: *Historical artefacts discovered and discussed by children from both parts of town. Some progress made in 'bridge-building' objective.* How's that sound?'

'Yeah, that sounds just great Ted. Sums it up nicely.'

Ted typed it out one-fingered, a look of intense concentration on his face.

'Right. Final whistle at...5.13 precisely. Anyone for a jar? It's European night down The Feathers.'

Then the meeting broke up. Miss McFadyen went back to her marking, David to his curry for one, and Big Ted to his usual stool by the bar.

Chapter Fourteen

October Half-Term
The Feathers

Ted walked into the bar and looked around. There they were, in the corner, in the middle of what was evidently an animated conversation. Their glasses indicated that the pair had been there for some time. 'Half-full /Half-empty?' thought Ted, as he made his way over.

'Evening Chas, evening Dave. Oh! Chas and Dave! Rabbit, rabbit, rabbit, eh?'

'Sorry Ted...?' Charles looked up at his head of year. 'Not with you.'

'Never mind. Cockney songsters of the late twentieth century. Ask your grandfathers-they'll tell you.'

'Not mine, Ted, he died in 2003,' said Charles, winking at David.

'Oh, sorry Chas. No offence meant. Pint of best lads?'

Ted returned with the three glasses enveloped in his huge hands, then set them down on the table. 'One for you, one for you, and last, but not least, one for me. Cheers, lads. Dave, d'you mind if we swap places? Like to keep an eye on the screen.'

'Who's playing tonight Ted. Anyone we know?' asked Charles, steadying the table as Ted settled into his new place.

'Nah. Two continental sides I think. Racing Fantasticos versus AFC Fuckwits of Denmark or something. If anything happens I'll let you know. So, you two were in deep and animated discussion. Nothing about school I hope.' He raised his glass and took a long draught before landing it back heavily on the table, now awash with 'best'.

'Young David here was describing to me the latest of his PSHE lessons and what his bunch are making of his weekly afternoons off- sorry Dave, educational trips- to the local museum. It seems...no, you tell him Dave.'

'I am all ears, as someone you've probably never heard of said to Noddy,' said Ted. 'Let's hear it, Mr Stacey.'

David went on to describe what the four youngsters had been doing over the six weeks of visits, how they had started to organise and document some of their findings, compiling their discoveries into a power-point presentation which they had given to the class just before half-term.

'Even though I say so myself, it was amazing. That Kirsty is a wiz on the computer, can do stuff I wouldn't be able to do in a million years.'

'Or in my case, a zillion years,' Ted contributed, before wincing at a near miss on the screen over David's shoulder. 'Open goal-should be shot,' he explained.

'They set it all up-all by themselves- all four of them working together. Even Alex and Lee. Just brilliant. The class were agog,'

'Good word,' interrupted Ted, and held up his glass in salute.

'and pretty much good as gold. No messing about, either before or during their presentation.'

'So, Mr History Detective, what did your young sleuths uncover? Something scurrilous and unsettling I hope. Haven't had much to talk about since *The Great Cricket Match Fiasco.*'

'Well,' David continued, 'nothing that would make *The Observer* as yet but, you know, good stuff which shows that the village has got a past, *has* done things together.'

'Won the bloody cup in 1916 if I remember correctly!' said Ted.

'Yeah, and lost men, Uppers and Lowers, in both wars, which seemed to come as a bit of a surprise to them all. Oh, and they were all interested in the old maps the kids found especially the ones showing places like the canal, Adam's Lock, High Trees, where Lee's mum works, and *this pub* you'll be glad to know, Ted!'

Ted gave a little nod of appreciation.

'Tell Ted about Tony, Dave- this'll make you laugh Ted.'

'Great-need a laugh following last half-term. Mind you, that centre forward is a joke if you ask me,' he said pointing at the screen. 'Tony who?'

'He started with us in September. Big lad. Spots.'

'Ah, Joyce; fancies himself as a bit of a winger, but got a nose that runs faster than he does. That Tony?'

'Just so,' said David, and resumed his story. 'So we've got to the point where the four kids are taking it in turns to tell the others about the visits. Lee wanted to talk about the canal, the lock and so on, so I let him. He was describing the fishing and wildlife and said we'd seen a heron and a few mallard. Joyce pipes up 'what's a fume allard?' so the rest of the class go crazy. Then, he just couldn't get his head round the idea that there was no plastic, or washing machines even, in Victorian times. He's definitely not a country lad-he just couldn't fathom it. The class thought this was great of course, and are calling him 'Fume Boy' now.'

Ted shook his head. 'And do *they* know that fume's a word even, I wonder? Okay, so we can take Tony Joyce off the Oxbridge Possibles list then-along with virtually everyone else in year eight.'

Ted rolled his glass onto its side. 'Ooh! Thank God it's empty, boys! Don't mind if I do.'

Dave offered to get the next round in and disappeared into the crowd by the bar. Mid-week football night was always a busy one in The Feathers and it took him a good five minutes to get himself noticed. In his absence Ted probed a little, asking Charles about David's project, how he felt it was going and what, if anything, he thought should happen next. Then David returned to the table and the conversation turned to other things, village tittle-tattle, sport and the like.

At just after ten David announced he had to be going. 'Up early tomorrow-off to see my parents in the metropolis.' He stood a little unsteadily.

'Come on Dave, just one more for the road!' Ted cajoled, but David was already putting on his coat and making for the door.

'Another time, Ted. Have a good break. See you Charles.'

And, with a half-wave, he pushed his way through the crowd and walked out into the October night.

*

David got up early, had his breakfast, then threw his sports bag and rucksack into the back of the car. It was only a short stay and some of his clothes were still at his parents' anyway, so there was no need to take a suitcase. It was a cold morning

139

and the mist hung like rags from the trees. He turned the car down the hill remembering, at the last second, to switch on the fog lights, then left the village for the open road, climbing the steep incline into the bright clear air of the upper valley. Below him, the houses had disappeared and only the spire of Our Lady's poked defiantly through the blanket towards the sun and heaven itself. He drove at a leisurely pace, taking in the beauty of the countryside, knowing that for the next two or three days he would be ensconced in the urbane 'sub-urbanity' of Muswell Hill, with its coffee-shops and its chic designer outlets. The Land of Plenty Inn came and went, and then he was surrounded by farmland proper. Within minutes, he had spotted a deer, a fox, and the sad remains of a badger. Above him hovered the now ubiquitous kites, circling patiently, waiting for their dinner. 'A pair of kites, a *couple* of kites, a *kettle* of kites-that runs off the tongue nicely, but does it make sense?' David mulled over the appropriate term before turning his thoughts to the coming few days.

At the seven o'clock beeps he was joining the A41 and the first of the many commuters he would encounter on his journey, east, and then south. It was the only time he felt smug for being a teacher, but still he'd exchange frustrated, understanding, smiles with the other drivers struggling with their mobiles as they slowed to a halt at the tail of yet another hold up. *He* had all day-all week in fact.

Leaving the joys of the A41 he opted to head cross country again, negotiating a winding route through quaint villages with their crosses and half-timbered houses, many now in mortal danger of their lives as ever-bigger lorries and coaches slavishly followed the instructions of their SatNavs. Signs for Hemel Hempstead and St Albans confirmed that he was heading in the right direction and he sat back to the mellifluous tones of Sir Terry Wogan and his breakfast show. And then he was back into the big traffic again, carried south in the torrent that was the A1(M). No time now for Sir Terry and his Togs. One hundred percent concentration required, unless you wanted to lose your mirrors, your front wing, or worse. 'But at least we are moving,' he thought as the river of cars ebbed and flowed, spurts of high speed dash brought to an end almost immediately by the bright red full-stops of brake-lights, reminiscent, he realised, of the marking he carried in the boot. And so to historic Barnet, a toe dipped in the shallow end of London. From here they watched The Blitz and saw the dark skies over the East End turn to red under the barrage of German bombardment. They died too, in their scores, as lazy bombers got it wrong or doodlebugs failed to hit their targets, arriving with deadly silence to shatter the peace of a summer's day, and evaporate the lives of their random victims.

Soon he was back in familiar territory, literally: his mother hailing from Whetstone, his father a child of East Finchley, and then onto the final tree-lined mile to Muswell Hill itself.

For a couple of days David decided to chill. His workbag remained firmly zipped and he spent most of his time mooching around the house and catching up with old friends who had chosen to stay in the area- generally taking it easy. It was a time to enjoy the comforts of the family home with hot water on tap 24/7 and cups of tea that appeared to come from nowhere.

Saturday night he hit the town-London Town- meeting up with friends from university. The usual things- couple of drinks and a meal, an alternative show, more drinks, Northern Line home.

*

Sunday morning. His footsteps thudded down the stairs.

'Mornin' mum.' He yawned and pushed his fingers through his hair.

'Good morning David-just. You look like something the cat's dragged in. What time did you get in last night?' She carried on peeling the potato in her hand.

'D'n know. One, half-one? Caught the last train and walked from East Finchley. Any toast?'

'Over there. At the moment it's still called 'bread' but I'm sure you'll manage.'

'Where's dad?'

'Where he usually is on a Sunday morning- reading the papers. Wouldn't disturb him while he figures out how to put the world to rights. Then you can save him from the crossword- don't know why he bothers, just makes him grumpy these days.'

David, put a couple of slices of wholemeal into the toaster and watched, waiting for them to pop up.

'If you're making a cuppa, I wouldn't say no. Don't offer your father one, it'll just make him want the loo.'

David laughed and filled the kettle, then spread his toast with real butter and Marmite.

'So, what's your news David? Haven't said a lot since you've been home.'

'Well, the flat's coming on. Painted the bathroom and kitchen as per plan. Car hasn't broken down yet, but *is* making a funny rattling sound. School's okay... classes behaving themselves, most of the time, staff keeping their heads above water. So, just the usual.'

'Nobody, *'special'*, on the scene yet then David?'

'Mum, if by that you mean 'do I have a girlfriend?' then no, I don't. And I do wish you'd stop asking. If anything happens, you'll be the first to know.'

'But David dear, you know I worry. You're twenty-eight, rattling around your flat, and all by yourself, miles away from home…'

'Mum! Stop it! It's only been six months since Claire and I, you know, split up and I need a bit of space. And besides, I don't 'rattle around' my flat. You've seen it-it's about the size of this kitchen!'

Deborah Stacey looked crestfallen and picked up another potato.

'Anyhow, how's Tina?' David asked, hoping to steer the conversation in a new direction.

'Your sister? I was rather hoping you would be able to tell *me*. Last time I heard she was lying on a beach somewhere near Sydney watching the sun go down. Party, party, party! I don't know what on earth she's doing with her life.'

'That reminds me of a funny story Ted told me about George Best,' said David. 'You know George Best, don't you mum?'

'Of course I know George Best, David- long haired lout of a footballer. Played for Manchester. Quite good looking as I remember it.'

'That's him. Well, the story goes-and I'm sorry if it's a bit racy mother- that he was caught in bed by a newspaper reporter, drinking champagne on ice with two former Miss Worlds, his red Ferrari parked in the drive outside. The reporter looked at him, shook his head and said, in all seriousness, 'Where did it all go wrong George, where *did* it go wrong?!''

David waited for the laugh, his mouth open.

'I really don't see what that sordid little story has to do with your sister. Pass me a carrot, won't you.'

David passed the carrots over and put his plate in the dishwasher.

'Listen mum, I'm going to get changed then head out for a walk. Need to clear the old head a bit. What time's dinner?'

A loud bleating and the sound of a tractor came from the radio.

'Ooh, thought I was home for a second!' David quipped.

'You *are* home, David,' his mother said with a stare, 'and dinner, *lunch,* will be on the table at one o'clock sharp. Say goodbye to your father before you go or he'll wonder where you are.'

David quickly changed then came down to the lounge where his father was surrounded by the Sunday papers- The Sunday Times for the news and The Express for a bit of light relief.

'Ah, David, you've emerged! How was The Smoke? Didn't get too...' he spoke in a stage whisper, '*rat-arsed*, did you!'

'Father! Shame on you! No, did have a few, but I didn't do anything the Department for Education could ping me for.'

'Well done, m'boy, well done. Right, try this one for size: 'Airman up for trial. Two words, four, then five.'

David thought for a few seconds.

'Test Pilot?'

The old man fiddled with his pencil looking from clue to crossword and back again.

'Yes, yes! That fits! School fees and all that have paid off, David! Well done!'

David looked around the room. Everywhere were reminders of his dad's time on the sea. The clock was brass and deep and at least sixty years old, a circular barometer making it one half of a matching pair. Above the mantle-piece was a glass case containing a huge array of nautical knots: the bowline, the sheepshank, the clove hitch and the memorably named, if not often-performed, monkey's fist knot. Elsewhere were etchings of tall ships, three masters, rigged and under sail, and on the piano itself, in pride of place, a black and white photograph of his father and mother on the steps of Buckingham Palace; in it, his father proudly holding the MBE up for the photographer to see- chest out, back ramrod straight.

'Going out, are we?'

'Well *I* am said David. Care to join me?

'No, no,' said his father quickly. 'Far too busy, lots to do.' He gave his son a wink and tilted his head sidewards.

'Mum's the word!' said David, noting the small sherry glass half-hidden beneath his father's armchair. 'I'll be back in time for din, for lunch.'

'Toodle- pip; don't catch cold,' said his father and readjusted his glasses, ready to tackle fifteen across.

David grabbed a scarf before calling goodbye and closing the door behind him. It was another lovely morning, autumnal fresh and just what his hangover needed. He made his way up the hill towards the back of the palace. 'Built in 1873 and then again in 1875' his father had reminded him earlier in his stay, 'burnt to the ground, almost as soon as it had gone up.' The imposing red-brick edifice looked proudly out over the whole of north London and way beyond, as far as Canary Warf and the City in the east, then to the BT tower and Camden in the west. And even further afield, as far as the London Eye and the palace's own distant cousin in the history of tele-communication, the hazy upright of the Crystal Palace TV mast.

The cup of tea promised, but undelivered to his mother, suddenly intruded on his thoughts, but was just as quickly gone as he scanned the view before him. He held his hand at arm's length and made a little 'o' with his thumb and forefinger. He squinted, like a marksman taking aim. 'Did you know, within that tiny space,' he muttered to himself, 'live ten times more people than in the whole of Hensford and its valley?' A couple passed and he dropped his arm quickly, rubbing his shoulder, as if easing an injury.

'Rugby,' he said by way of explanation, but by then the pair had gone. He continued to stare, taking in the view.

'When a man is tired of London': Johnson's words drifted into his mind. If the truth be told, David *had* become tired of London-but he had never really tired of life. He loved his new life, but coming back did stir something inside him from which, perhaps, he could never be completely free. 'Maybe it's because I'm a Londoner!' he hummed quietly in cockney twang, arms swinging, then surreptitiously looked over his shoulder in case the couple had finished their walk and were returning. He was alone. Alone, that is, but for the small figures he could see below him taking their dogs for their Sunday constitutionals, momentarily disappearing beneath the flat shadows of *Ally Pally,* and re-emerging into the sunlight a few seconds later.

He had never been one for the water, hadn't inherited his father's sea-legs nor his sister's wanderlust-not that he would have *inherited* this particular trait, exactly. But he stood at the centre of the Palace and looked down on London as his father might have looked at the vast expanse of the oceans- the captain of the ship, the ruler of all that he surveyed. And he thought himself at the centre of things, training his telescope and imagining the lives, the ins and the outs of all he could see. In the foreground, the green of the park gave way abruptly to the serried ranks of Victorian terraces. Hundreds upon hundreds, thousands upon thousands, each a home, a receptacle of stories every bit as rich and personal as that of the one he knew so well. Bounds Green, Wood Green, Hornsey Vale, Finsbury Park: was any other great city so keen to advertise its rural roots, deny the hard facts of concrete, bricks and mortar? And then, in the middle-ground, there were the posts, pillars and pylons, tell-tale signs of the spider's web of roads and railway lines, criss-crossing and chopping up the landscape into bite-sized chunks. It was too vast, too concentrated, to digest in any other form.

Needing to refocus, he turned his attention to the distant, hazy, monoliths of Canary Wharf and the crown of the Millennium Dome. And what of the stories told by the former inhabitants of that particular corner of the metropolis? The fading and faded memories of dockers, stevedores, prostitutes and pimps, spirited away, to be forever-traded for the bits and bytes of shiny hard-drives. Weigh them on the scales of modern London and its needs: no competition- end of.

Everywhere too, cranes scraped at the sky; spindly reminders, if one was really needed, that the story continues. Too slow to see from this distance, their jibs would move this from here, that from there, imperceptibly changing the shape of the very ground on which their continued existence depended. David strained, knowing it be futile, trying to see the cabs in which some tiny yellow-hatted man, would slowly change the face of the city forever.

And then there were the landmarks which his grandfather, and his grandfather before him, would have seen and recognised, even at this great distance. The dome of St Paul's, now dwarfed by its neighbours, defiantly poking its head above the trees. Always so many trees, the lungs of the city made visible. St Pauls: if the Germans couldn't cow her, then why should the Barbican, or the Gherkin succeed, however Teutonic-sounding the name?

And finally, there was the London Eye, peeping from behind yet more woodland- a roving eye, watching David as he looked back. It rolled slowly, providing vertical tours of the city while not moving an inch. 'Someone up there is looking at me,' he thought, 'oohing and ahhing; part of a leisurely loop-de-loop, at perfect right-angles to the turn of the world, three hundred feet below.' A dog barked in the distance bringing David back to the moment. He looked at his watch, and seeing it was ten to one, hurried his way back home.

'Hi! I'm home,' he shouted as he came in, hung up his scarf, and went into the cloakroom to wash his hands, ready to eat. The smell of roasting lamb assaulted his nostrils as he came in and he remembered why it was so important to touch base every so often- to unwind and re-fuel.

'Smells great mum,' he said. 'Can I help?'

'Take in the veg please dear, and be careful, the dishes are hot.'

David grabbed a teacloth and took two dishes into the dining room where his father was already waiting.

'Red or white, Dave?' his father asked, holding up two unopened bottles of wine for his son to see.

'As it's lamb, I'll have a nice glass of red please, dad,' he said, and sat down in his place, the one he'd sat in for as long as he could remember. His mother followed him into the room and laid the joint before his father.

'Your father will carve. And watch your fingers this time Robert-we don't want a repeat of a month ago.'

David's father held up his left hand, forefinger bent double, inwards and away from David.

'Tragic accident. I may never play the piano again.'

'Again?' said his wife. 'You never have.'

'Right, who's for the outside bit…?'

By half past one, David could feel the buttons on his shirt beginning to burst.

'So, tell us about that nice young man, Charles. How's he doing these days?'

'Well, mum, he's doing fine. Second in the maths department now and his wife's expecting a baby, in the spring.'

'How thrilling! A boy or a girl, or don't they know?'

'No idea. One or the other I think.'

'Never a truer word has been spoken,' said his father. 'Unless it's twins of course. And what about that other chap-big fellow, a Taffy, I think. Fred wasn't it?'

'No, it's *Ted* you mean dad. He's great. Same old Big Ted-always there with an anecdote, usually involving a pint or two. Great with the kids. And the parents too. Most of them just love him. Taught half of them. He's been there years, so he's part of the furniture.'

David's father motioned towards the middle of the table. 'David, pass us the uh, the oh, what do you call it, the'

'Cream?' David posited.

'That's the stuff!'

His wife rolled her eyes. 'How you manage to do *any* of those confounded crossword clues I'll never know! You'll be forgetting your own name next,' she said.

*

He arrived back at just after eight. As he pushed the door it snagged on the Hensford Free and a collection of envelopes, both brown and white, scattered across the welcome-mat. As he came into his flat he wished that he had set the central heating to constant- three days at home had soften him up already. He also wished that he had a cat to welcome him home, and, on going to the fridge, that he'd stopped at the mini-mart from some milk and biscuits. He turned on the kitchen light and sat at the table. A bill from the gas company, an advert for stairlifts ('surely for the previous owner', he thought), more bills and an envelope franked with the words 'High Trees Conference Centre'. He made a pile then searched for something to open the envelope- a pencil did the job, less than perfectly, but allowed him to take out the letter it contained.

'Dear Mr Stacey,' it read,

'Thank you for your recent correspondence regarding the possibility of a group visit to High Trees. Whilst it is not normal practice to conduct tours of the house, I have decided, in this case, to waive the rules. Given the young age of the participants I cannot stress enough the importance of good

behaviour at all times. Our clients pay good money for the use of our exclusive facilities and will expect the youngsters to respect the age-old dictum of being 'seen, but not heard'.

I trust you will ensure that this is the case and will see to all the practical arrangements including, and especially, those concerning the prompt departure of the children at the end of the visit.

Please report to the front desk at 1.15pm on Wednesday 28th November where my secretary, Miss Moloney, will meet you and make you comfortable. I will join you at 1.30 and take you around the house, finishing no later than 2.15 when I have a meeting. If there is anything else you wish or need to tell me regarding your visit, please do not hesitate to contact Miss Moloney at the number below.

Yours Sincerely,

H. Armstrong (Mrs)

David folded the letter back into the envelope and stuck it to his pin-board for safe-keeping. He phoned home to tell them that he had arrived, accepted their good wishes for the coming half-term, then settled down to an hour or two of brainless television before and getting an early night.

It had been a good break, and he was ready now for haul up to Christmas, and the challenge of the long, dark days to come.

Chapter Fifteen

Sunday March 16th 1800
Near The Lock

It was a cold, clear day in early spring and William was sitting on the canal bank, alone with his thoughts. Sunday school had finished some two hours earlier and he had asked permission from his parents to walk by himself along the canal as far as the quarry. They agreed and the rest of the family had stayed on to help the vicar clear away and do some work around the church grounds. William enjoyed the solitude near the quarry and would sit on the bank and think back to the many months of hard graft he and his father had put in to help complete what many were now calling this 'wonder of the modern age'. It gave him a deep sense of pride to think that he had been part of that team of men, old and young, who had helped transform Hensford from a sleepy backwater to a bustling village placed firmly now on the map of England.

William sat, half dozing, with his prized hat pulled down hard to keep the bright spring sun from his eyes. The only person he had seen was an itinerant tramp walking on the far side of the canal, his worldly goods stuffed into a brightly coloured sack carried at the end of a staff across his shoulder. The barking of his dog had startled William, and he had woken suddenly to be reassured that he was in no danger. 'The old fellah'll do you no harm, young sir. And besides, he's afraid of water, and cannot swim!'

William had smiled, raised his hat and wished him good-morrow. He watched as the old man disappeared from view on his way to the next place on his travels-poor in what he possessed, no doubt, but rich in life's experiences. Then he settled back and continued to doze, and thanked the Lord that he, at least, knew where he would lay his head that night.

'Ho! Canal-boy!' A sudden cry startled him for the second time that morning. 'I thought I'd find you here!'

 The voice was one he recognised as that of Adam Clarke, and he swung round to find the son of his master standing over him, smirking, his right hand firmly gripping a riding crop. His muddied boots and warm jacket told William that he had come on horseback and William thought he heard two horses neighing and whinnying to each other just beyond the trees.

'Bible classes over then, are they?' he goaded, slapping the palm of his left hand gently with the leather whip. 'Ma and Pa allowed you out to sit on the mud before your Sunday dinner, did they? What's it to be today then, boy- a few potatoes and a bowl of pigs' swill?'

'What do you want with me, Adam Clarke?' William growled and stood to face him. The other boy took a small step backwards and brought the whip up to the level of his shoulder. 'Don't do anything stupid will you, canal-boy. Just remember who my father is and why it is you get to live in that-what shall I call it?-*cosy* little house of yours.'

William felt his fists tighten but kept them firmly behind his back. Adam Clarke held all the aces and both of them knew it. If William were to speak his mind or, God forbid, let his fists do the explaining, then what would become of his father's job, and with it, his family's means to survive?

'That day in the coach. On the way back from Barnet,' said Adam, looking into the distance.

'What of it?' replied William, flatly.

'You made me look a fool, a coward. In front of my very own father. I don't forget things so easily, canal-boy. So today, I have come to teach you a different sort of Sunday lesson. Teach you mud-shifters that it doesn't pay to cross me, Adam Clarke, of High Trees! Tu comprende, canal-boy?'

 'My name's William-William Parker- and I'm not afraid of you Adam Clarke! Now, be away with you and your fancy language. Go! Leave me in peace!'

'So, not afraid are we? Not afraid-unlike the chickens you share your kitchen with! Chickens that scurry away to hide when someone so much as claps their hands! Brave or not, I need to show you who's boss, boy. To teach you a lesson in life that you won't forget in a hurry!'

And with a rush the canal owner's son raised his whip and brought it down hard across the face of the smaller boy. William cried out and took a step away, away from his assailant, and towards the muddy edge of the canal bank. A vicious second blow cut his other cheek and he struggled against the pain to stay upright. As Adam stepped forward to deliver a third stinging rebuke to his rival, William thrust out a hand and grabbed blindly at his jacket. In the tussle which followed the pair slithered towards the edge and tumbled with a great splash into the cold waters of the canal.

Both boys gasped as the freezing water snatched away their breath. Adam fought to rid himself of the heavier boy whose hands, in a frantic attempt to stay afloat, were gripping ever-tighter around his neck. Down, down, they both went in a frenzy of kicking legs and flailing arms. William felt the breath being sucked out of his lungs and screamed at Adam to let him go, but in doing so took in yet more of the canal's muddy water. The riding crop appeared in-front of his eyes and he made a grab, a desperate grab, at anything that would keep him from a watery grave: a grave that he himself had helped dig with his own two hands. Adam's legs were now sinking fast, his boots filling with the canal's deadly load, as William fought to get his head from beneath the other's knees. This was a struggle for survival and William strained every muscle in his canal-digger's body to loosen the grip of the other boy's hands and take his fill of the clear, life-giving air above.

As quickly as he had gone under, William's head suddenly broke through the now churning surface of the canal and he was able at last to gulp down the air he craved. With the strength only a dying man can muster he kicked off his rival, swam to the bank opposite and grabbed a handful of weeds which were hanging over the water's edge. His lungs screamed for more air and his body coughed and retched in his effort to expel the liquid back to where it belonged. As he slowly reclaimed the life that had been so nearly taken from him, his mind replayed the events of the past two minutes. Two minutes in which his life had streamed past his eyes: The early years spent playing at his mother's feet. Finding his *own* feet. Helping in the small vegetable plot beside their dank and crowded cottage. Walking and talking with his father. Sunday school and learning the word of the Lord. The births, the deaths, of brothers and sisters who never saw their first birthdays. His parents' tears. The beginnings of the canal. His first day proudly working alongside his father and the other men. The horses. Barnet Fair. The highwaymen...

He dragged a soggy arm across his eyes and felt the sting of the whip upon his cheek. With a start he came to his senses again. For the love of God! Adam! Where was Adam?

William forced himself to turn towards the canal once more. No sign of the other boy.

'Adam!' he screamed, looking around desperately. 'Adam, where are you!'

Through the murky waters his eyes could just discern a shadowy figure turning slowly some four feet under. At that moment a leather riding crop broke the surface, like the sword of King Arthur that William had heard about many times sitting, as a little boy, upon his mother's lap.

Weeping, William pushed away from the safety of the bank and swam to the point directly above the shifting shape near the bottom of the canal. Again, and again, he plunged his face below the surface, peering through the muddied water, now beginning to clear. At last, he saw it-Adam's face, mouth open as if crying for help, eyes staring, amazed, looking past him, towards the sky; towards the heaven he so despised. The neckerchief he wore so elegantly against the cold February air drifted lazily in the current, gently tapping his cheeks as if to wake him. He looked ridiculous, death mocking him where he lay trapped at the bottom, by a root, by a branch, or the weight of his own guilt...only God could say?

One more time, William dived down and tugged as hard as he could and for as long as he could at the arm of Adam's fine jacket. But, it was useless. Adam was dead. Drowned by the canal his father had sacrificed his own life to build.

Adam was dead.

William came to the surface, sobbing in his grief and with the agony of his efforts, managing to drag himself painfully onto the same muddy bank on which he had been sitting peacefully only minutes earlier. Shivering and crying, he started for home and, had he been able to think straight, may have heard the sound of two sets of hooves disappearing rapidly into the distance.

*

It was little Rosie, running ahead of the family, who sounded the alarm. The door, half-open, creaked gently in the breeze and William's hat was not hanging on its customary hook, just inside. Peering into the dimly lit house the little girl had noticed that the light, however meagre it was, was reflecting off the hard floor and she had touched the pools tentatively with her finger to confirm they were indeed water. Silently, following the trail of evidence, she found a pair of mud-drenched boots, soaking breeches, a badly- torn shirt and, finally, her older brother sitting alone, shivering, beneath a large blanket, ripped off his bed. He had said nothing but stared blankly into the embers of the guttering fire, a haunted faraway look in his reddened eyes.

Frightened, she had run screaming, back up the canal to where her mother, father, brother, and baby sister were sauntering happily homewards.

'Come quick! Come quick! Hurry! It's our William! Something bad has happened and he sits alone and will not speak!'

Without asking for further explanation Jethro had run as fast as his legs would carry him, shouting to Lizzie to be as quick as she possibly could. Lizzie gripped the baby she carried more tightly and picked up her skirts so she too could get to her eldest child without delay. Little Daniel cried and tried in vain to keep up.

Jethro arrived at the house first, and ran along the short passage to the main living space where he knew William would be. In an instant he took in the piles of wet clothes, the stale stench of steaming cloth, the staring eyes of his son and the blood about his face.

'In the name of God, William, what happened to you my son?' he said softly through his own tears, and pulled the boy close to his chest. 'And your face-who did this to you, Will? Will! Who did this?'

But William could say nothing, and fell immediately into a deep and troubled sleep, comforted only by his father's love.

Chapter Sixteen

Later That Day
Near The Lock

The sun had made its way lazily half way across the clear blue sky and the surface-waters of the canal were still once more, disturbed only by waterfowl cruising the canal in search of something to eat. Swans made their way smoothly past the point where William had lain only hours earlier and a moorhen pecked inquisitively at a riding crop wedged amongst the reeds, before losing interest and moving on.

The prow of a rowing boat appeared in the distance and the far-away voices of two local men, enjoying their few hours break from work in the fields, drifted through the still air. As the boat hove into view an observer would have recognised them as brothers- Alfred and Tom Harper- enjoying their favourite past-time of fishing on this, their only day of rest from work on their father's nearby farm. It had been a quiet day on the water and the fish had not been biting but they chatted and joked regardless, happy only to be free of the toil of hard labour, enjoying the peace of a fine spring day.

As the boat's gentle bow-wave caused the riding crop to bob up and down momentarily, Tom, the older of the brothers, suddenly exclaimed, 'Fred, stop rowing, there's something in the water! It's a body, I'm sure of it! Stop the boat!'

The younger brother pulled back on his oars and the boat slewed to an unsteady halt.

As both peered over the side into the shallow depths of the canal they knew what they saw. With a single look, and without exchanging a word, they made ready to raise the corpse from the water. Tom looped a length of rope, left coiled at the bottom of the boat, into a makeshift noose while Alfred steered the tiny vessel into a position alongside the shape below, using one of his two oars like a punter's pole.

Leaning as far over as he dared, Tom attempted to secure what would be the saddest of catches while his brother steadied the boat as best he could with the oar. After several minutes of trying, Tom finally looped the noose around a leg and he was able, with Alfred's assistance, to free the body enough to drag it slowly towards the bank from where it had presumably made its final, fateful journey. When it was safe to do so Alfred jumped to the bank and tied the boat up to the trunk of the magnificent Weeping Willow under which William had dozed earlier that day. Both then began the back-breaking work of dragging the body out of the water and onto dry land. Even for two hardy farm-workers the effort was very great but driven as they were by compassion and fear they at last pulled the unfortunate victim, face down, onto the bank.

After some minutes, during which the brothers lay motionless and exhausted, Tom announced gravely it was time they completed their task. Gently, and with great respect (for the brothers were God-fearing men) Tom turned the body over so that the face rolled towards the open sky. Both gasped as they recognised the boy as Adam, eldest son of the most important person they knew.

'Dear God above, Fred, it's Master Adam!' said Tom, crossing himself and grasping his brother's arm for re-assurance.

A blackened eye and deep scratches to his cheeks were evidence that young Adam had died fighting for his life, and the gold fob-watch still visible in his waistcoat pocket told them that if this had been an attempted robbery the boy had put up a brave fight, leaving his attackers disappointed. But the hat in his hands- soft leather, with a blood-red band- was not his. It was not the headwear favoured by a gentleman of the times- but it *was* strangely familiar. Tom looked at Alfred, amazement and disbelief in his eyes, as Alfred, understanding, turned away and was violently sick on the grass.

*

The banging, when it did arrive, came as a shock but little surprise to those in the lock-keeper's cottage. William was still asleep, occasionally moaning the name of Adam before his flickering lids closed again and he returned to whatever nightmare was playing before his eyes.

Bang! Bang! The door opened, and along the short corridor and into the room walked Jack Burrows, ex-canal worker, and now Constable of the Parish of St James's. In his hand he carried a large wooden staff, symbol of his authority, and behind him shuffled a small number of local men, sent to assist him in the arrest.

His eyes met Jethro's, and the pain of the task he was about to perform was clear to his former foreman.

'Jack. What brings you here?' asked Jethro, the even tone of voice disguising the terror gripping his heart.

The other touched his hat, and thought he spied Elizabeth and the children weeping quietly in the corner, the gloominess of the room making it difficult to see clearly after the bright sunshine of the day outside.

'Jethro, it is not you I seek, but William-your son.' He held a soft leather hat out in front of him, a drop of water falling onto the hard floor like a tear. 'It's Master Adam, Jethro. William has drowned Master Adam!'

Chapter Seventeen

The Following Day
The Lock-Keeper's Cottage

It was over twenty-four hours since William had been taken away and Adam had breathed his last. And then, what Jethro had been expecting and dreading more than anything else other than the dreadful fate of his eldest child, actually took place.

The family had been sitting in the lock-keeper's cottage in a silence that was almost deafening and which threatened Jethro's very sanity. The happy world of children's voices and busy fingers was but a distant memory, and all was now doom and gloom. Without warning, the door of the cottage was kicked open with a force so great that a hinge was ripped from the wooden frame and splinters flew across the floor. Lizzie screamed, and the briefest of silences was followed by the crying of children and the angry shouts of men's voices from the passage outside.

Jethro quickly took to his feet, ready to face what he knew was to come-Edmund Clarke and his men streaming into their home.

'So here you all are, one great happy family! Jethro Parker, doting father to a murderer, surrounded by his kith and kin! And where is *my* eldest son, Jethro? Where is he who would be the next head of the Clarke family? Where is he Parker, damn you? Where is he now?'

His eyes were red with fury and lack of sleep. His lower lip quivered as he struggled to contain the emotions built up since the awful news of Adam's death had been broken to him and his unbelieving wife. He stood, unable to move, his hands shaking by his sides. Behind him three men, two burly estate workers and the long figure of Saunders, his most trusted servant, blocked the door. Saunders, Lizzie noticed, would not meet Jethro's eyes and stared fixedly at the hard stone floor.

Jethro looked at his boss, a man whom he had once admired above all men and by whom, he was sure, he had been loved in return; and the words he had prepared all but failed him.

'Mr Clarke, Edmund, I know not what I can say other than to proclaim my son's innocence. I cannot explain what occurred yesterday but I swear, upon the Holy Book which I hold most dear, that William is *not* a murderer! He has not one bad bone in his body and would not-*could not*-take another man's life. There has been a dreadful, dreadful mistake!'

'A mistake?' spat Mr Clarke. 'Damn your eyes, Jethro, there are none so blind as those who will not see. Isn't that what your good book says? I will see him hanged like the common criminal he is. He shall be strung up on a gibbet for all to see! And you, Jethro Parker, and what is left of your scurvy brood, are to be out of this building by nightfall or, God help you, you will have me and my men to answer to!'

At this, the two men accompanying Saunders stepped forward from the shadows. Each man carried a hard wooden cudgel with which he slapped his free palm rhythmically, making sure the gang's dark intentions were now as clear as crystal.

Jethro fell forward onto his knees before his former master and friend, his head bowed and his hands joined in supplication. 'I beg of you, please don't do this to us Edmund! Where will we go? What will happen to my wife and children, innocent of any crime, each one of them? For the love of God spare us the workhouse Mr Clarke. I entreat you to be merciful and leave us not to starve!'

But Jethro's words fell upon deaf ears, and by the time he had raised his head his former master had left the house, and was striding towards the carriage waiting to carry him back to High Trees, where his eldest son lay in a coffin of Hensford's finest oak.

Chapter Eighteen

Tuesday March 18th 1800
Hensford Lock-Up

The door swung open and a hand thrust a bowl of steaming gruel towards the prisoner. William's eyes flickered open at the scrape of metal on stone and he turned slowly to see the bowl sitting in the middle of the cold, hard floor.

'Make the most of it,' said the voice from the other side of the door, the bolt slamming into place, 'where you're going, it's the best you'll be tasting for many a month!'

William knelt on the floor and put the bowl to his lips. The warm liquid was a comfort and he hardly noticed, let alone cared about, the tasteless slops with which he was being fed. Using his fingers he wiped the bowl clean and then licked the inside to make sure that not a morsel remained. Then he leant back on the rough straw mattress which had been his bed the previous night and closed his eyes. Never before had he felt so alone. Never more scared. The awful events of the previous Sunday played over and over in his mind. If only he had run away when he had had the chance. If only he had not grabbed his assailant's coat. If only Adam had not grasped him so fiercely when the two had fallen with a splash into the freezing waters. If only. And now, here he lay, the blood of his rival upon his hands, rotting in the village lock-up. He clasped his hands tightly together and started a fervent prayer to God to have mercy on him and upon his family. He carefully rehearsed the words of The Bible he knew he must now commit to memory, the ones that if recited properly before a judge could save his neck: Psalm 51 learned from years of study in the Sunday school at St James'.

'Be merciful to me, O God, because of your constant love. Because of your great mercy wipe away my sins! Wash away all my evil and make me clean from my sin!' he began, and uttered all seven verses before rolling onto his front and sobbing uncontrollably into the fetid straw.

Sometime later, a shaft of sunlight, slanting through the one tiny window high on the wall of his cell, woke him again from his uneasy slumber. It took him a few moments to remember where he was, why he was not waking in his own bed close to his family, why a cruel hunger gnawed at his empty stomach. Then the living nightmare began once more and he held his head in his hands and wished that it were he, and not Adam, who was dead.

Time dragged slowly that day as he counted the church bells tolling the passing hours, and longed to hear his mother's voice, to feel the strong arm of his father about his shoulders. 'Where are they?' he thought, in his despair afraid that even they might have forsaken him to his fate, abandoned their 'murderer' son just when he needed them most. But, at the point he felt he could take no more, his dark reverie was broken by the muffled sounds of raised voices, somewhere beyond the barred door of his prison cell. One sounded as if it might be his father, but he could not be sure.

'Father! Father! I am here!' he cried, and got no answer; but beyond the thick walls of the lock-up an impassioned argument was taking place.

'I have strict orders from Mr Clarke 'imself that nobody- and I means nobody- is allowed to see the boy. More than my job's worth to go against a man like Mr Clarke. And that's an end to it. Orders is orders.'

The man was unknown to Jethro. Not a face he recognised. Almost toothless, and unshaven, he stank of cheap brandy. He rose unsteadily to his feet. He was a giant of a man and not one to be argued with. He leered at Jethro and sat down again on his rough wooden bench slapping his palms together noisily as if to signal 'and that is that.'

Jethro took out a small purse that he carried inside his shirt and placed a single gold sovereign down hard on the bench. The other man pretended not to notice and waited until Jethro slapped down a second, bent close, and whispered something into his ear.

'Well, you never knows does yuh?' answered the giant and eyed the coins blearily before picking one up and biting down with one of his few remaining molars. Satisfied that the gold was real, he stood up and started towards the back of the building. 'You got ten minutes, and not a second more. And not a word to a soul or I'm a parish pauper and your precious son will be ready for the drop!' he said grinning, and mimicked the action of a noose tightening around his neck.

Jethro pushed past the man as he unlocked the door to the cell, then cried out the name of his son as they fell into each other's arms.

'Ten minutes, mind! And no more,' the voice said as it returned to its bench and contemplated what it would do with its ill-gotten gold.

In the cold cell a few moments passed before either could speak. It was Jethro that broke the silence as he assured his son that he would move Heaven and Earth to get him out of the stinking hole in which he now found himself. And then, hardly daring to ask, he begged him to tell him what had happened in those fateful hours and minutes by the canal, just two days earlier.

Once William had composed himself, he described how he had been dozing beneath the willow and had seen not a soul apart from a passing tramp. He went on to tell his father how the older boy had struck him in the face with a whip and how they had fallen together into the freezing water. When he arrived at the point where Adam's eyes stared heavenwards, wide and amazed with his mouth agape, it was too much for him to bear and he broke down again upon his father's shoulder.

Jethro hugged and kissed his eldest son and felt overwhelmed by the love only a parent can truly know.

'Will,' he said, trying to be strong for his son and himself, 'you are innocent of Adam's death. You are guilty only of defending yourself from a brutal attack and in the eyes of God, William, it is Adam and not you who was at fault.'

'But dad,' William said in a whisper, 'who will take the word of a poor wretch such as me when it is the son of Mr Clarke that lies at the bottom of the canal? Who will believe the son of the lock-keeper? It is finished dad. It is *finished*!' he added more loudly.

The voice sounded at the door once more.

'It is indeed finished-ten minutes is what I said and ten minutes is what I meant! Now I'll be pleased if you could leave the prisoner to his own thoughts and me to my luncheon,' he said, before belching and wiping his mouth on the sleeve of his rough jacket. 'Now, be out with you!'

Reluctantly, and with a heavy heart, Jethro stood and hugged his son, promising him he would do whatever it took and more to see him free again. Then he left without a further word, leaving the gaoler to his bread and cheese and to the pint of cheap brandy bought with his precious sovereigns.

*

Two weeks passed before William was loaded into a locked wagon for a journey that would take him to The Gatehouse in St Alban's, the bleak prison in which he would be held whilst awaiting his trial for Adam's murder. No quilted leather interior this time and no springs to smooth out the ruts and potholes of the long, lonely road at the end of which he would discover his fate. He sat, bound hand and foot, in the back of a simple wagon, the only comfort being a layer of straw scattered on the uneven wooden floor. What little light there was pierced the cracks between the planks which made up the walls, but he was unable to see any of the countryside through which they rattled steadily eastwards. Sounds, which had been denied him in the lock-up, now served only to taunt him further and confirmed, as if he had needed reminding, that he was no longer a free person. The happy voices of children playing at the roadside, cattle lowing in the fields, and the sound of geese and ducks flying overhead all made his darkness darker and the cords that bound him tightly, tighter still. And in his mind he could not escape being haunted by the memories of an earlier trip, to Barnet, when Adam's face mocked him on earth as he now did from beyond the grave. Hungry and thirsty, William pushed himself hard into a corner, to disappear further into the shadows, to hide from those who would have him dead.

And in the warm April sunshine a new lock-keeper and his family were moving in to the house the Parkers had once proudly called 'home'. A small girl, three years old perhaps, came running to her mother's side clutching a pretty straw doll that she had found, discarded by the previous family, whilst the man of the house surveyed their new accommodation and reflected that one man's loss was indeed another's gain. In this fast-moving age of opportunity, good fortune must be grabbed with both hands —and let The Devil take the hindmost!

In another part of the valley Jethro Parker and his family looked to the kindness of neighbours and to old friends to sustain them in this, their hour of greatest need. Old favours were recalled and room made for this family ripped apart by the tragedy unfolding around them. Lizzie and Rosie were taken in by a kindly old spinster from the plaiters' school, Daniel was left with a distant cousin, and Jethro himself found sanctuary on the flagstones of St James'-a floor which he himself had swept clean the previous Sunday. Another day. Another life. But all knew that this would not and could not last. The kindness of the village could not be relied on forever; and besides, some were starting to whisper darkly about 'helping the family of a murderer' and how this might be viewed by another, more powerful, family: the Clarkes, at High Trees.

Adam's Lock

Chapter Nineteen

Thursday October 21st 2010
Lower School Corridor

Ted heard her before he saw her. The raised voices of an irate parent and office staff were unmistakable, and Ted made his way quickly down the corridor to the main reception. The voices grew louder as he approached, the words more distinct, the aggression more apparent.

'I've had enough. It's an f'n disgrace and I'm taking them both out if somefing ain't done about it *now*.'

The office staff, safe on their side of the glass, looked up desperately as Ted arrived.

'Oh, '*im*. Now what?'

Ted took a deep breath.

'Ah, Mrs Hill. Maybe I can help?'

'It's Ms. Maybe you can, but if you can't I'm writing to Ofsted. It's a bleedin' disgrace, and me and Wayne-his dad- won't have any more of it! The twins come home every night and it's always the same story. Bullying this, bullying that, and it's doing my 'ead in!'

'Well, Ms Hill, we can't talk here. Come to my office.' He indicated the way with a flourish and Bex marched off, down the corridor she had known since she herself had been a pupil of the school some fifteen years earlier.

'Wendy, could you join us please?' Ted said to one of the more experienced secretaries.

'Oh, and you'd better bring a pad (*and a baseball-bat*, he thought).

Ted followed the angry parent into his office where she stood clutching a bag to her chest. She rocked rapidly from foot to foot, and her face continued to twitch with the pent-up emotion.

Ted stood and waited.

'What?' she said, feigning a look of surprise. 'What d'you want me to say?'

(*Nothing*, he thought) and invited her to sit down on one of the low, comfy chairs. 'Sit here where we can be a bit more comfortable. Now tell me what the problem seems to be.'

'There ain't no *seems to be* about it Mr Richards,' she said, dumping the bag on the floor beside her. The mobile phone it contained went off on cue, strains of The Birdy Song adding a touch of the surreal to the early stages of the proceedings.

(*Just let it ring,* thought Ted, *a bit of background music will help make the party go with a swing*).

Wendy, the secretary arrived and stood by the open door.

'Come in Wendy, close the door and take a seat. Ms Hill was just about to explain why she's so upset.'

'Call you later, babes, I'm at school,' said Bex, before clumsily switching the phone to silent, and stuffing it back in the bag.

'You were saying (*or screaming*),' smiled Ted weakly. 'Before we were rudely interrupted.'

'Yeah, whatever.' She turned round to look at the secretary. 'What's she doing in here? Scared I'll do somefing, or somefing?'

'Mrs Thorpe is here to record what we say so that I can concentrate on your every (*moronic and aggressive*) word,' Ted answered, reassuringly.

'Right, but I'm not having her writing things that ain't true.'

(*Best keep your mouth shut for the duration then, Bex,*) he thought, but assured her that Mrs Thorpe was an experienced secretary who would record only what was said. 'She's not here to cast an opinion' (*though I could tell you exactly what it was, if you were interested*) he added.

For the next twenty minutes, Bex read out a litany of grievances, scrawled out on a piece of note paper (apparently torn from a school text book, Ted observed) detailing all the injustices that had been visited upon Dominic and Theresa, the twins.

'And another fing...' the list went on and on, and Ted listened quietly, nodding and occasionally asking for clarification. 'Aren't you listening?' Bex snapped, to which Ted explained that he was 'reflecting back' (*you dozy cow*) to be absolutely sure he had understood correctly.

At one point Bex's non-stop tirade brought on a fit of coughing and Ted asked Wendy to fetch her a glass of water. (*It's a drink, like Special Brew, but with a more subtle taste,* he nearly explained.)

'It's them f'n Uppers. Always at it, givin' it this, givin' it that.' Her fingers opened and closed, yapping for effect. 'And you teachers are worse than useless-always siding with the Uppers, your sort of people.'

Ted raised a large hand and held it in a 'Stop' sign position. 'Whoa! Just stop there. I'm a Valleys boy myself-The Rhondda (*South Wales- go as far as Watford, turn right, and keep driving*) and I grew up on a council estate. My grandfather did forty years down a pit and died of lung disease, so don't start talking to me about *'your sort of people'*. And don't forget who runs the football team around here!' His open hand turned into a stabbing finger. 'Let's keep to the facts, and we'll see what we can do, eh?'

Bex looked a little cowed, and for the first time shifted uncomfortably in her seat. Mr Richards was a big man, *kinda intimidating* she had to admit.

'Whatever. I'm talking about *my* kids. Don't care about anyfing else.'

'Okay. I'll look into what you said (*when I have five spare minutes, which could be never*) and I'll give you a bell to say what we've done. How's that sound, *Ms* Hill?'

Bex got off her chair and grabbed her bag. 'S'ppose so, but if nothing changes I'm going to Ofsted and the kids'll be home educated.'

'That's your choice *(and I'll inform social services, if you do)* Ms Hill, but let's hope it won't come to that. Now then, Mrs Thorpe will show you to the door, and I'll be in touch soon. Byee.'

The secretary stepped aside to allow Bex to pass, fiddling in her bag for the phone, then rolled her eyes at Ted as the device kicked merrily back into life a little way down the corridor.

Ted went back to his desk and sat down heavily on the faux-leather office chair he'd managed to get out of the school's furniture budget. It was only then that he became aware of the beating in his chest, the tightness in his jaw, the cold sweat on his body. His fingers drummed gently on the desk-top before making their way slowly to the larger of the two drawers. Opening the drawer, just enough for his hand to enter, he felt for the reassuring shape of the glass neck, the familiar cool of the bottle. He paused, then started to unscrew the cap, humming a tune as he did so: it was the opening bars from 'You've Got a Friend'- baritone, adagio, in E-flat Major.

Chapter Twenty

Friday October 29th 2010
Our Lady's Church

His funeral was never meant to be like this. Family members, a few close friends, his colleagues, and a selection of ex-pupils perhaps. But not this.

The school had been closed for the afternoon and all pupils encouraged to pay their last respects. Hundreds lined the street leading to the church, many wearing the black and white of Luton Town Football Club. Here and there the red and green of Wales lent a touch of primary colour to what was otherwise a drab, grey, day.

The hearse rolled slowly past the shops of the high street, past Patel's newsagents, Parker's locksmith's, and The Feathers, before turning right onto the final approach to Our Lady's. The crowd watched in silence, some holding scarves aloft on straight arms, gently rocking from side to side, but most just stood, watching the approach of the cortege, unsure of how to react, unsure of what they should do. Uppers and Lowers waited shoulder to shoulder, their differences forgotten, for today at least. And striding ahead of the hearse, with unparalleled dignity, the town's principle undertaker led the way, black top-hat upon his head, tails drifting gently in the wind, silver-topped cane held stiffly in his right hand. 'Big Ted', proclaimed the flowers adorning his coffin. It was all that was needed.

The hearse edged carefully below the low roof of the lychgate, a tight squeeze, and crunched the final hundred feet to the main door of the church. A second car followed closely and then a third. One by one, the cars emptied- Ted's sister from Neath, big-boned and ruddy like her brother, his small, widowed mother, some cousins from the Bristol area- no more. And then the bearers, David and Charles amongst them, stepped forward to shoulder the coffin. The undertaker checked they were comfortable before giving a solemn nod that signalled the start of Ted's last journey on this Earth. The eight mourners took the strain, careful not to lose their footing on the gravel, and headed for the church door and the aisle beyond. They took particular care at the steps, adjusting their positions before carrying on.

Inside, the organist had been playing some of Ted's favourites- a selection of Welsh hymns, The Floral Dance, and one by the singer James Taylor that everyone could recognise but nobody could put a name to.

Finally, the coffin came to rest on the metal bier, and the bearers stepped aside, bowed, and took their places in the pews. David and Charles sat together. 'My God, was he a big man or what?' David whispered to his friend and Charles smiled, silently nodding his agreement.

It was David's first time in a Catholic church. He took in the ornamental decorations: the statue of 'Our Lady' from whom the church took its name, the enormous crucifix hanging high above the altar, the stations of the cross, and the weak autumn sunlight coming in through the stain-glass windows, just catching the gold of the tabernacle which occupied the centre of the altar.

'The grace and peace of God our Father and the Lord Jesus Christ be with you,' the priest began, to which all replied 'And with your spirit'.

The service continued, following The Order printed on the cards placed on the pews in readiness for their arrival. Psalms followed readings, and communion followed prayer, with the small figure of Father Murphy directing proceedings with a predictability and solemnity befitting the occasion. David listened and watched, aware of the fact that this was a part of Ted's life of which he was totally unaware, an essential element of which he was not, and could never be, a part. What else was there, what thoughts, what ideas and dreams, which made up Ted's life but would go with him to the grave, unrealised and unresolved? He suddenly woke from his reverie.

'And now, Charles, a colleague of Ted's, is going to say a few words on behalf of all Ted's family and friends.'

Charles stood and went to the lectern by the altar rails. He steadied himself, removed the piece of folded paper from his inside jacket pocket and, after clearing his throat, started to speak.

'Good morning everyone, and an especially warm welcome to Ted's family who have travelled here from South Wales, and from Bristol, to be with us on the occasion of Ted's funeral.' He looked in their direction and received nods in reply.

'Where to begin? Ted was a big man and played a huge part in each and every one of our lives- not just those who have gathered here in the church this morning, but all of those listening to the speakers outside. And thousands more too, whose lives he touched over the twenty-eight years he was a teacher at Hensford High- or Hensford secondary, as it was known in the nineteen eighties, when he first started teaching.'

He paused.

'Ted was born in Porth, in The Rhondda valley, on mid-summer's day nineteen-sixty, and welcomed into this world by his mother Gwyneth, father David and big sister Lillian. He was a big baby, in the real sense of the word, and was, if Lil's stories are true, a bit of a handful about the house!'

Lillian nodded in recognition, then took out a handkerchief and dabbed the tears from her eyes.

'He went to the local primary school where his teacher reported that, and I quote, 'Edward fails to see the point of writing. He prefers to kick a ball about and treats most things as a joke'. Some things never change.'

A laugh rippled through the congregation, releasing some of the tension that had followed the coffin into the church.

'I am afraid things did not improve much at secondary either where one report confirms that Ted, notice the change in name, was guilty of 'spasmodic application', in English, I think it was. Ted loved words, but didn't much like writing them.

'However, all was not lost. Ted excelled at sports and used his great size to his advantage. At six feet one he was a shoo-in to the under-fifteen rugby team but was, in fact, more of a footballer than a rugby player. His school, alas, was very much your traditional Valleys secondary with a headmaster who thought soccer the work of the Devil and refused, point-blank, to allow any football teams to represent his school. Football, when it was played at all, was done surreptitiously behind the gymnasium, like smoking, where the headmaster could turn a blind eye and still retain his dignity.

'Ted also had a natural flair for technical subjects and, seeing a way to earn a living without having to write much, threw himself into woodwork, metalwork and, as it was called then, technical drawing. As I know his family will attest, Ted proved himself to be a talented craftsman producing chairs, bookcases and the like for the family home. In later life he continued with this as a hobby, and anyone who visited his office will recall the finely carved coffee table which took pride of place near the window.

'So, at the age of sixteen and with a clutch of O- levels under his belt, he embarked on the path which would eventually lead him here, to a village, and a valley, many miles from home. A-levels in Woodwork and Technical Drawing, and a re-sit in English O-level, were just enough to secure him a place at Cyncoed teachers' training college, in Cardiff, where he spent three happy years, most of it, if reports are to be believed, playing football and (how shall I put this Mrs Richards?) enjoying the liquid refreshments, to quench the dry throat, which inevitably followed the games, of course.'

Charles turned over the paper and smoothed it against the dark wood of the lectern.

'So, why Hensford? Well, I asked him this very question myself, not so many months ago. The truth of the matter is that it was the first job he saw in the Times Educational Supplement. He noticed that it was in a valley, found Hensford on a page in his AA book, and decided to go for it. It was too far to come and see it first, so he just applied, then hoped for the best. A few weeks later, an invitation to attend interview arrived in the post and he made his way, a big journey in a small car, up the M4, to the school. He was met by the then head of department, a Mr Keiller, who took to him at once and, hardly bothering to interview him, virtually offered him the post on the spot. Things were different then!

'Ted settled in well- took to the job 'like a duck to water', to quote the man himself. He liked the kids and they, it was clear, loved him back. With Ted they knew where they stood. He'd call a spade a spade, but was always the fairest of men you could ever meet. That was the kids' perspective and that was the view of anyone who worked with him- it was cards on the table, upfront, and honest.

'The rest is history, and far too much to relate this morning. He went from strength to strength and rose up the ranks, eventually becoming head of Design and Technology and, lastly, Head of Year. He never lost his love of technical subjects and managed, just, to keep up with developments. Computers were never really his thing, but he marvelled at what the pupils were able to do and show him in their 'virtual' worlds. But his real strength was not in making objects, but in forging relationships, and in moulding people to be the best they could be. People might have admired his craftsmanship, but they *loved* his humanity.

'So, what will I remember about Ted? There's so much to remember. I'll remember his sense of humour- the way he could see the funny side of things, just like his primary school-teacher observed when Ted was still in short pants. But when he needed to be serious, when things got rough, as they do from time to time, he was always there-solid as a rock. And a big rock at that. I'll remember his love of people and his easy-going style. Ask anyone, that's what they'll tell you. I'll remember his passion for sports-any sport...apart from cricket! He just couldn't see the point. "It's too slow" he'd explain. If all the sports in the world were laid out like a great big banquet, he once told me, cricket would be the breadstick poking out of a pot at the end.'

This brought a laugh from every corner of the church and a split-second later from the hundreds outside.

Charles stopped, and cupped a hand to his ear. He pointed.

'There you are- that's what he meant to the people of Hensford. There's your evidence, if you needed it.'

'So,' he continued, 'Big Ted's gone but not forgotten. Never will be, not by the hundreds and thousands that were privileged to know him. RIP Ted, Rest in Peace.'

Then he picked up the paper, nodded to the priest, and returned to his seat. As he sat down David lent over and patted his knee, giving him the thumbs up.

'Very nice Charles; very nice,' he whispered.

Father Murphy stood and returned to the centre of the altar steps.

'Thank you Mr Murray. Ted was evidently a much-loved man. And now, we all stand for The Concluding Rights.'

The congregation stood and turned to the last page of their booklets.

'Receive his soul and present him to God the most high,' they said in unison.

'The Lord be with you,' the priest responded.

'And with your spirit.'

The priest then looked up and made the sign of the cross towards the people, intoning, 'May almighty God bless you, the Father, and the Son, and the Holy Spirit' to which all replied with a final 'Amen'. He then invited them all to join in singing *Bread of Heaven,* one of Ted's favourite hymns, and later to join the family, in the back-bar of The Feathers, for some simple refreshments.

As the singing came to an end, and the organist played more of the favourites, the pall bearers once again lifted the coffin and carried it carefully to the hearse waiting outside. The family followed and eased themselves into the cars which were to accompany the hearse to the cemetery just half a mile away, on the far side of the canal near Clarke's quarry. David and Charles opted to walk knowing they would arrive comfortably in time for the interment. The crowds thinned a little but those remaining stood and clapped as their favourite teacher passed on his final journey through the valley town he had come to regard as home.

Rain started to fall and the wipers finally removed a white rose that someone in the crowd had thrown onto the screen earlier in the day.

*

When it was over a small gathering made its way to the back-bar of The Feathers. A long white-clothed table was set with a modest array of sandwiches, quiche, and pie- Ted's favourite. His face looked out from a photograph, *Ted Richards, 1960-2010* written in italics on a small card leaning delicately against the silver-gilt frame. Groups stood round and swapped stories of Ted's early life-some touching each other gently on the fore-arm and agreeing that it really had been a lovely service.

Charles and David stood to one side, each balancing a cup and saucer in their hands.

'What would Ted make of this?' David asked, nodding to the tea. 'A cuppa- in the back bar of The Feathers- he'll be turning in his grave.'

'Yeah, certainly would. Place won't be the same without him. It's going to need some big feet to fill his shoes...' Charles' voice trailed off, a sip of tea substituting for the full stop.

'Right. I'm off,' said David needing to escape the forced gentility of the occasion. 'Books to mark, lessons to plan.' Tomorrow, school would be open and life would go on.

He picked up a breadstick and snapped it in two, giving one half to his friend.

'For Ted,' he explained, before turning his back and walking out.

*

The following Saturday, seven thousand fans, twenty-two players and a selection of match officials and ground-staff stood and applauded for a full minute.

The caption below his photo read 'Ted Richards- The Hatters' BIGGEST fan.'

He'd have liked that. He'd have died happy.

Chapter Twenty-One

Thursday November 3rd 2010
Head of Year's Office

Ted had been buried a week and Charles appointed head of year 8-temporarily, at least.

David knocked on the door, the nameplate now read Mr Murray, and Ted's Luton Town photograph returned to his family.

'Come in!' Charles shouted, not looking up from the computer. 'Oh, hi Dave. Come in. Sit down.'

David came in and sat opposite his old friend. 'Suits you well, Chas. Just sad about the circumstances.'

Charles bade him stop with a firm wagging of his finger. 'No way Dave. I'd give everything not to be in this seat. Boots too big to fill. Needs to be someone else.'

David relented, back-tracking as he realised his faux-pas. 'But seriously Chas, Ted would not have had it any other way. You were his blue-eyed boy. The son he'd never had.'

'These eyes are brown Dave, in case you'd never noticed...but thanks, all the same. Let's sit on the comfy chairs.'

The two sat next down and David ran his hand over the smooth top of the coffee-table.

'Beautiful finish on this table, Chas. He was a real craftsman and despite all his bluff and bluster, a bit of a perfectionist.'

'Sure was Dave, we'll not see his like again. He was one of the old school, an artisan turned teacher- he could have made a decent living turning out pieces just like this, but he opted to help the next generations instead. What a bloke.'

'So, what's been going on since you've been in the big man's seat?' David probed a little more, wary of pushing it too far.

'Well, nothing more from Ms Hill- 'the Bex woman' to you and me. All went quiet when the circumstances of Ted's death came out...guilt maybe? I don't know, but I hope it doesn't have any repercussions for the twins. Not their fault their mother's a lary cow. Couldn't help noticing how the two sides seemed to come closer-the Uppers and Lowers I mean-after the funeral. What a legacy that would be, eh? What d'you think?'

David slipped down the chair, pressing his head into his hands held high behind his neck. 'Good point Chas. Does seem to have been a bit of a 'rapprochement', a reconciliation maybe. But it could be just a short-term thing. It could all kick off again- the next football match, a wrong word overheard in the pub, a girl 'dissed' by a boy from the other side of the valley.

It's a tinder box, Chas, and Guy Fawkes is approaching fast, if you know what I mean.'

'How's the project going, Dave? Any mileage there? What about an assembly-you know, something to remind them of Ted's passion for the village to come together, how 8S are leading the way? What d'you think?'

David came back to sitting, properly, as his mother would say. He leaned forward and picked up a biro from the table, then tapped away furiously on the edge, hoping for inspiration, or simple clarity at the very least.

'Don't know. Are they ready for it yet? Not sure. Let me sleep on it Chas, and I promise I'll get back to you.'

'You're a gent, Dave; now if you'll excuse me, I have an appointment with a data-spreadsheet.'

'Ooh, enjoy,' said David, then made his way back to the staffroom for a coffee, a biscuit, and another think.

Chapter Twenty-Two

Friday November 4th 2010
David's Classroom

It was six thirty and the school was quiet. David was glued to the screen of his laptop when a voice brought him back to the moment.

'Penny for them, Mr Stacey?'

David jumped and looked up to see the familiar figure of Alistair, the school caretaker- or 'Site Manager', as it now stated at the front gate.

'You made me jump Al! Creeping about like that.'

'Creeping? I've been standing here, leaning on my brush for at least two minutes, David. It's half-past six. Past your bedtime. Time to knock it on the head for the day.'

David looked at his watch, then apologised for keeping him waiting.

'But before you lock up, have a look at this...it'll only take five minutes.'

The caretaker gave him a weary look, then stood behind him, looking over his shoulder.

'Five minutes…right, let's see then: a bunch of kids- they're standing on the stage- assembly time. Fascinating. Now can I get home, or 'er in doors will be having me guts for garters as they say.'

David pointed at the screen.

'Yes, Al, but look closely at the faces. Who's that at the front?'

The caretaker bent closer and slid his glasses onto his forehead.

'Can't properly see. It's a boy. Could be anyone.'

'Yes, but that's just the point Al! It isn't *anyone*. It's Lee Parker!'

'And?'

'And, Lee Parker has never-and I mean *never*- spoken in front of an audience before. When stage –fright was being doled out, he was the one at the front of the queue asking for more. He *hates* being the centre of attention like that!' said David, warming to his theme. '*And*, he's a Lower, surrounded by Uppers! It's amazing!'

The caretaker humphed and looked at his watch.

'Al, this was Big Ted's assembly. The one I told you about?'

The caretaker dragged over a chair and sat down.

'Beggin' your pardon, David. I didn't realise. The one you did in memory of Mr Richards? So, how did it go?'

'See this one? The tall lad with the fair hair? That's Alex Clarke- supposed sworn enemy of Lee Parker.'

'He's got his arm round his shoulder,' Alistair said, 'don't look much like enemies to me.'

'Exactly!' observed David. 'But the families have hated each other-or so they say- for as long as anyone can remember. You're not a local are you Al?'

The caretaker put on an exaggerated Midlands voice. 'I'm a Brummie, me. Can't you tell? Brought up in the shadow of Spaghetti Junction.' And then, in his usual voice, he explained that he had moved to the valley for the love of a local girl. And then he'd married his wife.

David laughed.

'Right, so you'll know all about the Uppers and Lowers, and how they just *love* each other?'

'Don't they just, David,' he replied. 'Worse than West Brom and Villa fans. Too hot to handle.'

David seemed not to be listening and pressed the play button. The white, background noise of a thousand teenagers suddenly subsided as the two boys stepped forward to the front of the stage. Lee held his hand in the air, waiting until the room was completely quiet.

'I taught him that!' beamed David, and then quietened himself as he waited with the others for what Lee had to say.

'Right. Thanks.' Lee looked at a crumpled piece of paper which he held in both hands. David detected a slight tremble, but visible only to the camera, he thought.

'So, we have come here today to remember Mr Richards who was our head of year and one of the best teachers in the world, I think so anyway.'

He peered at the paper; in the back-row somebody coughed.

'He was a really kind man and I think he looked on us like his own children. He didn't have any of his own,' he explained, 'but still knew how to talk to young people like us. And that was really good. One thing he hated was when people are unfair and we all knew what he thought about bullying and that sort of stuff. Even about the Uppers and Lowers problems.'

A few people shuffled in their seats and a low murmur rippled through the hall. Lee fiddled with his paper, but waited until it had died down again.

'Taught him that too.'

'So, we, Mr Stacey's class I mean, have been doing some searching about- no, research I mean- about Hensford and what things have happened in history which are about everyone in the village.'

He stopped, self-conscious at his lack of lucidity, and handed over to Alex.

Alex stepped forward and scanned his audience before clearing his throat and speaking to the back of the hall.

'As Lee just said, we are here to honour the memory of Mr Richards or, as *we* all knew him, Big Ted.'

A few people laughed, helping to ease the tension that had built up in the room.

'He *did* hate bullying and he *did* hate prejudice of any kind. And... he supported Luton, which made him one of us, wherever he might've come from!'

This time loud laughter rang through the hall as people relaxed into Alex's story until an urgent *shush-ing,* coming from various corners, established the silence again.

'So now, we are going to tell you what it is that we have found out about Hensford- the place which Mr Richards made his own, the place he left Wales for, so many years ago-because he loved the valley, the village, and its people.'

David paused the video and turned to the caretaker.

'What do you think of it so far?'

'Powerful stuff, David. Even *I* am amazed at seeing that lot up there, and I'm not even a local.'

'No, neither am I, Al. And I'm amazed too.'

He pressed the play button again, and the two watched as one by one, boys and girls, uppers and lowers, stepped forward to explain what the four class-representatives had found out on their visits to the museum. The photograph of footballers in their long shorts and even longer moustaches drew the inevitable remarks and guffaws, but no-one was disrespectful of the occasion and everyone was secretly proud of the team's achievements. And when it was explained that this was at a time when millions were dying for their country across The Channel, the noise died down again allowing the story to continue. Kirsty and Jo did their bit too, linking arms as they took centre stage and reading a short poem they had written in praise of Mr Richards, Big Ted, and his love for the valley. As they came to an end David blew his nose noisily, hoping Alistair would not notice the reddening of his eyes, whilst the caretaker himself quietly brushed a tear from the corner of his own.

'Thanks girls.' It was Lee again. 'So, that's our assembly. I hope you all enjoyed it, even the sad bits about Mr Richards. So, as we go out, Alex is going to put on some music. See you on Monday.'

And as a thousand, rather subdued teenagers, left their chairs, the strains of *'You've Got a Friend'* drifted through the air and followed them out of the hall, down the corridors, over the fields, through the streets and back-alleys, across the canal and into their homes; in whichever part of Hensford they happened to live.

*

'Sounds wonderful Dave!'

'It was, dad. I don't think anybody spoke until they had left the school grounds, and even my own class were strangely quiet as they left the stage. I couldn't really speak myself much- it felt like being in church, or watching something momentous on the telly- like Lady Di's funeral. Or maybe something a bit more hopeful, like 'Children in Need'- I don't know, but I feel it really got to the kids in a way that none of us could have foreseen.'

'Just sad that it had to be as a result of such a tragic death. How old was he again?'

'He was fifty.'

'No age.'

'No. A real waste.'

'But it sounds, with your help, that he's left quite a legacy. Well done; you should be proud, Dave. Right, got to be going.

Your mother's shouting for something so I'd better look busy. No peace for the wicked!'

'Thanks Dad. See you soon,' said David and put the phone back in its cradle. His father was right, he should be proud, and deep down, proud is what he was feeling right now. And proud, too, that his father was proud.

He walked over to the window and put off the light. Over the Chilterns, the sky was huge and black, and below him the town's lights twinkled, reminding him it was still there. It was a cold Saturday evening, and most sensible people were out enjoying themselves, or indoors, watching whatever reality shows they preferred-the choices were endless. Suddenly, his thoughts were interrupted by the crack and fizz of a huge firework, the dazzling crown of which filled the sky. 'My God,' he remembered, 'it's November the Fifth!' and at that point he realised that his journey, from child to adult, was finally complete.

Chapter Twenty-Three

April 1800
The Gatehouse, St Albans

William woke from a disturbed sleep as his wagon rumbled to a halt on the rough cobblestones that formed the central courtyard of the St Alban's Gatehouse prison tower. The bolts were slammed back and the door swung open drunkenly allowing the cooler air of the night to fill William's mobile cell. He propped himself up on the hard floor and felt in his bones every rut and every pothole he had endured between Hensford lock-up and this, his new temporary accommodation.

'On your feet, boy!' growled a new voice and one with which William would become only too familiar over the coming months. William shielded his eyes as the light of a lantern filled the space between him and the speaker. He squinted painfully, doing his best to make out the features of the man who addressed him- a commanding silhouette, standing legs apart, and filling the doorway of the carriage. The right hand fingers closed thickly around the handle of the flickering lantern while the left clasped a large bunch of heavy keys which jangled and clanked together as the figure rocked from one foot to the other.

'Untie him,' were the next words he heard before two lackeys scuttled past their master to cut the ropes that bound William, allowing him to stretch his legs for the first time since leaving Hensford.

'You know the rest!' said the man curtly before stepping down and disappearing into the night once more. The two workers listened as their master's footsteps grew fainter, and they waited until they heard the slam of a door on the far side of the courtyard, before speaking.

'Blimey! The Gaffer's in a right old mood tonight, Boz. Full moon affecting 'im again, d'ya think?'

'Nah. It's the cold. Nights are startin' to draw in and ya knows he 'ates the winter. And 'im with 'is big log fire an' all that! What abaht us poor wretches, freezin' 'alf to def. No better than the flamin' prisoners, we aren't! Anyways, wot we got 'ere then?'

William shrunk further into the shadows and said nothing.

'Cat's got his tongue, Jed!'

'Cat eh? That'll come in useful for catchin' the mice then won't it! Always says that don't we Boz! Right young sire, let's get you out of your fine carriage and into somewhere a little more comfortable,' he continued, causing Boz to laugh darkly at his comment.

'Don't you go listening to him, he's half crazy!' Boz said next, then 'Welcome to The Gatehouse Inn-St Albans! Your final stopping place on the way to... well who's to say, sir? To meet your Maker or maybe to make the acquaintance of a nice young Aborigine girl in far off Aus-tra-li-a!' He broke the word strangely into its four syllables. 'Don't know which one's worse, Death or Botany Bay!' he roared, before the pair grabbed his arms and half-dragged William towards the huge doors of The Gatehouse itself.

After hours bound in the back of the carriage William's body ached horribly. He limped across the uneven cobbles, occasionally stumbling in the blackness of the courtyard, kept upright only by the rough support of his two companions.

The one he now knew as Jed released his arm and swung open the door into the building proper. Smoking candles weakly lit the way up a set of stone steps and along a narrow corridor, to the place that was to be William's room that night and for many more to come. The sound of their footsteps and voices mixed together and echoed strangely as the three approached the studded door to the cell. William, too scared and too tired to put up any resistance, slumped to the floor as, not for the first time, a door clanged shut behind him.

'Sweet Dreams!' shouted Boz coarsely as their mocking laughter and footsteps disappeared into the still of the night. 'Sweet Dreams?' Where had he heard that before? He thought, confused, his mind taunted by the echoes of that first night in Barnet.

Nothing stirred and William sat stiffly, almost too terrified to breathe, against the rough wall of his cell. He felt blindly about him and found nothing but rough straw and the hard, damp floor. He breathed out slowly and brought his fingers to his eyeballs and then pressed them firmly into their sockets. Tears pricked his eyes and rolled slowly down his cheeks to fall silently onto his breeches. Then a heart-rending sob, the like of which he had not known since he was a small boy upon his mother's knee, welled up from deep within this young man's chest, and he fell once again to the floor, crying noisily.

'Who's there?!' said a startled voice in the darkness.

'William shook himself awake and pressed his body hard against the wall. He scarcely dared breathe again and flicked his eyes from left to right, but all he saw was the deep black of the night- and nothing more.

'I says, who's there?' the voice demanded again, this time with a touch of menace.

William sensed that it came from his left and turned his body to face in that direction.

'I'll do you no harm, sir,' ventured William, his terror preventing him almost from speaking at all.

'My name is William. William Parker.'

The other grunted and William heard a movement like someone straining painfully to sit after lying for a long time- a discomfort he knew himself only too well, this last two weeks.

'I'm trying to get some shut-eye! This is my cell and I don't take kindly to strangers wakin' me in the middle of the flamin' night. Where you from?'

'Hensford.'

'Never 'eard of the poxy place. What you in for?'

'In for?' William asked feebly.

'Yeh, what you in for? What did you do! Slit a man's gizzard? Steal a sheep? Make a pass at your master's daughter? Why you here! You musta done *sumfink* wrong!'

William paused and pondered his response. Why *was* he here? What had he done that was wrong? What had his father said to him about 'in the eyes of the Lord'...?

'I don't know,' he said. 'I don't think I did anything wrong'.

The other man laughed gruffly and spat. 'Look young sir-'ow old are yuh?'

'About fourteen years I think, sir,' answered William.

'Right, fourteen or whatever year-old William, we's all in 'ere 'cos we'did somefink bad. Me? Took a man's silver and brained 'im in the process. Swanky man he was, all airs and graces. Didn't oughta 'ave upset old Bill Perkins though -not when I had a skinfull of best ale! Anyhows, he lives to tell the tale and gets his money back and I'm rottin' in The Gatehouse waiting to learn me fate! It's the rich that gets richer and the poor that gets poorer, and make no mistake. So, that's my tragic story-what's yours?'

William wiped his eyes and dragged his sleeve across his nose and mouth before speaking again into the void. He started slowly and with many a pause but when he got to the part where Adam was standing over him, whip in hand, the words poured out of his mouth much as the water of the canal had poured into Adam's. He spoke to the darkness hardly aware of the other man listening and stopped only when he had told it all and reached the moment of the gatehouse cell-door slamming behind him and hearing the frightening voice of 'old Bill Perkins'.

Bill spat again before he spoke.

'Sounds like quite an adventure, young master Parker. More's happened to you in two days than 'appens to most in a lifetime. Must be tired out.'

William confirmed that he was and would be pleased if he could now be allowed to sleep. The other man- now his cellmate- told him that he needed to rest but that he might find there was more than just the two of them sharing their room that night. William, startled at this news, looked around desperately into the black hole of the cell, listening for evidence of others, only to be told mockingly that whatever fellow 'prisoners' there might be in the cell scuttled around on four or six feet rather than two, and couldn't speak the King's English!

That first night William slept precious little. In the wee hours, when the room seemed at its darkest, and the one thin blanket provided proved useless in keeping out the piercing cold of the damp cell, William made his acquaintance with the rats and the fleas which made up the remaining 'clientele'. For them the cell was basic but quite acceptable accommodation. For the rats, the straw scattered on the floor provided comfortable bedding and the thick walls gave shelter from the rain and wind. Even the tidiest of eaters- and many of the prisoners had eating habits which would have shocked Adam, even - could not help but leave morsels of bread here and there, soon to be gobbled up. And of course a clever rat would not be confined to a single cell but would start his meal in one, scamper off next door for his main course, to finish in a third cell for dessert. A rather monotonous but adequately filling diet, thank-you very much. As for the fleas and bed-bugs they were the scourge of every living, and dying, prisoner. It was not long before William joined Bill in scratching and slapping away at the tiny torturers living not near, but actually on, their

215

itching bodies. William had experienced fleas before, of course, but nothing like these. The only saving grace was that the torment that they inflicted stopped him from thinking of anything else, and for the first time in many hours his focus was on the here and now and not on the awful events of yesterday, or the frightening uncertainty of tomorrow.

Chapter Twenty-Four

The Next Day
William's Cell

The next morning, William was woken by the crowing of a cockerel in a nearby farm. Whatever weak sunlight there was struggled to illuminate the inside of the cell and William squinted as he tried to make out the layout of his new abode. Bill appeared as a large heap, snoring and cursing under his breath as another flea enjoyed an early breakfast, and William resolved to let the other man sleep for as long as he possibly could. The cell itself was larger than he had expected, but was devoid even of the few meagre comforts he was used to at home. Both men had the same rough blankets to keep out the cold although William noticed, much to his discomfort, that Bill appeared to have three blankets to his one. In the far corner of the room was a bucket which William knew, to his disgust, was to be their only toilet. A rough wooden bowl lay on the floor next to his cell-mate as well as a small cup half-filled with small beer, a watery version of the ale served in taverns and inns around the town. William then realised just how dry his mouth was feeling, but dared not slake his thirst using the drink of his cell-mate. Who was to know what the other man might have done to him. Hadn't he already asked him about slitting a person's gizzard? Better a dry throat than no throat at all.

Close-by a bell rang out the hours: one, two, three, four, five, six, William counted. Six o'clock, and the large heap that was Bill shuffled ominously to the sound.

'Wha? Wha? Wha's tha?'

He rolled over and peered, bleary eyed, at where William sat, eyes wide-open, against the wall on the far side of the cell.

'Who?... Ah! Now I recalls!... Young William Parker-villain and murderer, isn't it? Sleep o'right?'

William watched intently as Bill struggled into a sitting position and took a noisy slug of the brown liquid in his mug.

'I have had worse-but only one the night they took me away from my family,' replied William, and started to cough violently, his throat as dry as the straw used to make his sister's only dolly.

''Ere, 'ave a mouthful of this,' said Bill, and offered the cup to the youngster. 'That's one thing they do give you 'ere- beer, till it comes out of your ears if you want it. Food's lousy though, and if the fleas were 'orses they'd be pulling carts- big buggers they are! Did they send you a welcoming committee last night?'

William told him they had and that a rat had run over his face at some point during the small hours. Bill laughed and told him he'd have to get used to it. Every prison he'd ever been in (and there had been a few) had rats. Some were worse than others. St. Alban's was a rich-man's city- nice Cathedral that you could see just outside the barred-window of the cell- and the rats were a better class than you might get elsewhere.

'Very well-mannered these St Alban's rats. Never known one to bite…yet. Must be all that Bible talk they get from the church just there,' he said, pointing at the window. 'Be grateful for small mercies, that's what I say, William m'boy!' and Bill chortled in that mocking way William was starting to get familiar with.

As the light improved, William finally got to see the face of his cellmate. It was a dark, weather-beaten face, suggesting years spent in the wind and cold: a farm worker, a navvy or boatman perhaps, but William decided it best to keep his thoughts to himself for the time being. Bill was a serial prisoner-a bad man, who must have done many wrong things over his life- and William concluded it was safer to let the man tell his story at his own pace. It would not do to make an enemy of Bill, with a thick door and a barred window between himself and the outside world, and only rats and fleas to call on for help if his cellmate were to turn nasty.

'Whatcha lookin' at boy?' asked Bill, when he realised the youngster was studying his features. 'Never seen a sword cut before?'

William flinched as the other man turned his face towards the window and a shaft of sunlight caught the thick red line of a jagged scar that ran from the top of his ear to his chin. William thought of the mark left by the whip brought down Adam on his own face, and how that had hurt. How much more would the cut inflicted upon Bill's face have hurt and what sort of a monster could have done such a thing?

'I beg your pardon, Bill,' he stammered, 'I did not mean to stare and I meant no offence. The light is bad and I cannot see so clearly.'

'Ah, 'tis nothing boy. A cat can look at a king, or so they say. You hungry?'

William, to that point, had not noticed the hunger which filled his stomach. He had not eaten, and barely drunk, for a full day and night. Fear had made him forget his hunger pangs and in truth he had no real appetite for food.

'You got to eat when you can in 'ere William m'boy. Never know when your next meal might find its way into someone else's grubby mittens. Place is full of thieves and villains. Wouldn't believe it, would you!'

Bill threw William a hunk of bread he had in a sack-cloth bag that he slept with under his head. William thanked him, and gobbled it down before the other man could change his mind. Feeling he could trust him, William asked him about the prison routines, when they were to be fed, if they were allowed out of their cell and so on and so forth. Bill spoke like a father to his son, or like a teacher to his pupil, guiding him in the ways of the place and, most importantly, how to keep himself safe.

'There are some you can cross and there's others you want to steer well clear of. Take Boz and Jed- they're nothing to be scared of. You keep on their good side and they'll leave you be. They spend their time doin' other people's bidding. Not an intelligent thought between them. I've seen cleverer things pulling carts across muddy fields.' For the first time in what seemed like years, William heard himself laughing. It was a strange, alien feeling, and he almost looked over his shoulder to find out where the unfamiliar sound was coming from.

'And what of The Gaffer?' William asked, when he had regained his composure.

'Ah, The Gaffer. Now there's a strange kettle of fish, William my boy,' Bill said quietly. 'The Gaffer is one of the ones you never want to cross- a cruel master without a kind bone in his body. When The Gaffer comes a-callin' even the rats scurry away and hide their whiskery faces where they can't be seen.'

He took a swig of the beer he had next to him. 'Nah. You don't want to cross The Gaffer.'

William felt a chill come over him, pulled his blanket a little closer around his shoulders, and made an oath to himself that he would be a as good a prisoner as he had been good son before he was taken away from his family. Better to keep your head down and do as you were told than to risk having it knocked off by the man with the keys.

Chapter Twenty-Five

Some Days Later
William's Cell

Nearly a week had passed since William had first made acquaintance with Bill and the two had quickly grown to trust each other. For Bill, William's arrival had provided some relief from the daily boredom of the dank, dark, cell, and the young lad was certainly better company than the last villain he'd had to endure (till the latter was taken off to be hanged or transported, Bill never knew which.) And for William, Bill behaved like a sort of strict uncle, gruffly keeping him on the straight and narrow, and making sure he did not get into unnecessary trouble with The Gaffer or his dim-witted helpers.

One morning, Bill caught William staring at the scar on his face again and, reading the questions in the young boy's eyes, he started to talk…

'I was a slaughterman, William, a butcher by trade. South coast, not far from Portsmouth. Nice little business I 'ad and made enough to keep me'self in beer and tobacco. Me old man had been a butcher before me, and his dad before 'im. We had it going back down the generations. Wouldn't be surprised if it was one of me grandfathers who slaughtered the fatted calf in the Bible story! Know that one boy?'

William nodded that he did know the story- the tale of the son, a sinner, who was lost, then returns to his family. When he appears over the hill they arrange a huge feast in celebration- welcoming him home with hugs and tears of great joy...but he said nothing of this, fought back his own tears, and allowed Bill to continue with his tale.

'Anyhows,' said Bill getting himself more comfortable, 'things were going just dandy when one night I was in The Ship Inn, me favourite watering-hole, doing what I does best : enjoying me'self, singing all the songs I'd picked up over the years and stealing a kiss from any pretty girl who happened to walk by. The beer had gone to me head and I said to me'self, Bill, enough is enough! Look after your hard earned cash and get yerself back 'ome before you gets yerself into bother. So off I goes on me usual way back 'ome, weavin' me way across the fields, avoidin' the woods on such a dark December night. All of a sudden, I feels a hand upon me' right arm and then another upon the left and I realise that I cannot move. I sees that I'm surrounded, and try as I did I couldn't move away. There must have been six, maybe seven of them, and I knew I was in deep trouble one way or another. I told them that I ain't got nothin' worth 'aving! and tries to get free but they was 'aving none of it. Your King and Country needs you, says the biggest and meanest of them and it's then I realised I was being pressed into joining His Majesty's Royal Navy...'

'It was press gang?' asked William, wide-eyed. He'd been told of the gangs of roughnecks whose job it was to catch and force unsuspecting men to join the navy, to fight the French or whoever else was causing problems to the British seamen as they strove to rule the waves beyond the distant horizon.

'Aye, a press gang indeed, young William, and as scurvy a bunch of cut-throats as you ever did see. So, I was not in any position to argue and soon found me'self bound for Portsmouth and a new life as ship's cook, plying the seven seas.'

He spat into the corner and wiped a sleeve across his mouth before continuing.

'The date? I'll never forget it. It was the second of May in the year of Our Lord seventeen hundred and eighty seven. I was introduced to His Majesty's Ship, 'HMS Serius', whose duty over the following 251 days would be to accompany the first convict settlers to be transported to New South Wales, in the land we now know as Australia. Over seven hundred convicts, men and women and their children, were stowed aboard half a dozen ships, and our job was to make sure that they stayed on board and were delivered safely to their new homes-far from England on the other side of the world. There was all sorts on those ships- thieves, sheep rustlers, beggars, boys younger than yerself who had done nothin' more than steal a loaf of bread cos they was so 'ungry and would have died otherwise. It broke yer heart to see them, but it was either that or rot in an English hulk to die of gaol-fever, or perish at the hands of a murderous cell-mate.'

William shuffled uncomfortably, but Bill just grinned and added that the boy had nothing to fear from Bill himself, however alarming the scar on his face.

'After three weeks at sea we dropped anchor at Santa Cruz on the island of Tenerife where we took on fresh water, vegetables and meat. Two long months it was before we made our next landfall in Rio de Janeiro, Brazil. And what a hellish two months that was! The further south and west we ventured the hotter it became, with the sun high in the sky, the winds light, and our progress deathly slow. The air was thick with moisture and it clung to our very skin driving all living things mad with the itching. Rats and other vermin, and bedbugs as big as peas, tormented us all and more than once I thought I should be better dead beneath the waves than alive on board! But I was lucky compared to the wretches who had to endure conditions below decks- they had no fresh air and no light, and many were driven to the very brink of insanity.

'We were one whole month ashore, buying provisions and filling the ships' tanks with fresh water. The women's clothes we had to burn, so infested and stinking had they become and they were forced to wear new garments fashioned from rice sacks. They felt even worse than they looked, the poor darlings! But much of South America belongs to the Spanish crown, William, and we did not care to stay any longer than was necessary. Does not pay to outstay yer welcome with people who not long before you were at war with! But we had little that they were interested in-no gold, no silver, no slaves for market, and they let us on our way. Can't say I was unhappy to see the last of the place, but we were heading East into the unknown, making for the Cape of Good Hope in far off Africa and then on to Australia, and the pleasures of Botany Bay.'

William listened in amazement to Bill's story as it unfolded. Tales of storms and high seas, with mountainous waves as high as the cathedral tower outside the prison window. Bill told how one night, when the moon was full and storm clouds scudded across the southern skies, he saw a sea serpent, as clear as he could now see William himself, swimming alongside the ship. Twenty, maybe thirty paces long it was, with large glowing eyes and a huge mouth filled with teeth the length and girth of a man's arm. Many a sailor had seen similar beasts, said Bill to a wide-eyed William, and some had never lived to tell the tale...

'But the main enemy was not sea serpents, Spanish pirates or even falling overboard to sink forever beneath the waves. No William, the main threat, the killer, was invisible to the human eye: Scurvy! I've seen men built like bulls, with the courage of lions, reduced to nothing more than shivering wrecks, teeth all fallen out, left with the strength of the babies they had come to resemble. 'Orrible it is to behold when the scurvy takes you.

No respecter of position either-captain or cook, prince or prisoner, Mistress Scurvy will suck the very life out of you, make you a shadow of your old self before spitting you out and leaving you to the sea-gulls.'

William gulped and wondered how it was that anyone could survive months and months onboard one his majesty's ships. If the storms and the rats were not enough, then scurvy, the scourge of seafarers the world over, would certainly do for you and send you to your Maker-and that, sooner rather than later.

'I suppose yer wondering how it is that old Bill Perkins lived where many another has perished? Well, I'll tell yer and it ain't no lie: fruit and vegetables! I swear, even with me being a butcher and making me living from the beasts of the fields and all that, but it's true! It was them that ate their greens and drank the juice of limes and lemons-and that ain't so easy I can vouch!- were the ones that got to set foot on the new world that is Australia. Those that did not found their final resting place in Davy Jones's Locker- the bottom of the sea, to you landlubbers. So, young William, do as yer old uncle Bill tells yer, and if you ever finds yerself Australia-bound, eat yer greens! Now, I'm tired and I'm goin' to have me'self forty winks, as long as the friendly bedbugs of the 'otel St Albans let me be.'

And with that, he rolled over and went to sleep, leaving William to daydream of exotic lands far away, sea-monsters, and the humble fruit that may one day save his life.

*

In the months that followed, William settled into the drab routine of life as a prisoner. Every day was the same, each a dull twin of the one before. The anticipation of food was a constant, cruel companion- in spite of the fact that in the free world outside the gates, swine would have spurned the contents of the bowls.

Bill had become William's best friend, and mentor, raising his spirits when the darkness threatened to drive him crazy. The older man taught him how to keep his head down, how to avoid trouble with the other inmates they met on their daily exercise walks around the prison yard and, critically, how to stay on the right side of The Gaffer and the brainless duo that was Boz and Jed. In truth, William never did see The Gaffer properly, save for the odd occasion when his heavy footsteps and the clank of keys forewarned of his arrival at the other side of the cell door. And even then, he never showed his face-just a pair of menacing eyes and his laboured breathing confirmed that he was watching you. As for Boz and Jed they were, in some ways, part of the entertainment, if that was the right word. 'Daft as a brush' was how Bill put it, and they would laugh quietly at the pair's antics and their obvious lack of understanding of life beyond St Albans and its prison. Bill, in contrast, had seen the world and was only too happy to share his experiences with William. Some days, for hours on end, he would tell William of his time on the sea-the things he had seen and the people he had met. On several more occasions, he explained, he had been part of the convoys transporting yet more miserable prisoners to the expanding colonies south of the equator.

'Another world, William', he once started. 'I saw things there you would not believe. Giant rats that hop around on their back legs and keep their young in a pocket at the front, birds in colours undreamt of in England, and sheep twice the size of anything you have ever seen before. Aye, and natives the colour of dark oak who are completely at one with nature-who understand the rhythms of the seasons in ways that we cannot fathom. They hunt. They fish. They know the names and the uses of every single wild plant and berry and use the bounty of nature to keep themselves alive in places where you and I would be dead before nightfall!' Then he went on to describe the prisoners he was responsible for on the voyages-the cargo who filled the holds below decks. When talking thus he was visibly moved by the stories that the prisoners had told him over the years. He spoke of young boys and girls, some younger even than William himself, sent away from their families for seven, sometimes fourteen years, for crimes as petty as stealing a silk handkerchief or a loaf of bread from a rich man's table.

'Good people, William, undeserving of the harsh punishment handed out by the courts unable to find prison spaces enough to accommodate them in England. Not every rogue is a rascal Will, and not every rascal a rogue,' he added, enigmatically.

On other occasions, Bill would talk about some of those transported who had made good in Australia, serving their time as honest, hard-working prisoners and earning the respect of the jailers. At the end of their sentences, some had even been granted their own plot of land or had stayed to work on local farms providing for the needs of the ever-growing numbers of European settlers arriving every year.

Then one day in August, and without warning, Boz arrived and cheerfully announced that William would be leaving later that morning.

'Time for you to leave us young William. Time to say your goodbyes to old Bill here and prepare to say hello to the judge and jury at Hertford Crown Court. You leave in half an hour and I'll be back to escort you to your carriage.' And with that he left, slamming the door shut behind him.

William slumped back on his bedding amazed. He knew all along that this moment would arrive but still it hit him hard; shocking him as Adam's blow had done many months before. Bill came over immediately from where he sat and cradled William in a way he had not been held since his father made his one and only visit to him in the lock-up. He wept, and shook, at the fear of what was to come, but also at the prospect of leaving Bill, his teacher- his rock. What would he do without him?

The cathedral clock struck one, and a few minutes later both Jed and Boz arrived to take William to the wagon, and whatever fate awaited him. Bill gave him one last hug and told him to be strong and to keep believing in whatever would sustain him over the coming days. With that, William was led along the dark passage that had first brought him to his cell, and down the steps into the bright sunlight of a warm summer's day. And then, across the courtyard where other prisoners waited in line, each one shackled and joined to another, making escape impossible. William was chained, ankle to ankle with a prisoner he did not recognize, then, in a macabre parody of a childhood game, shuffled forward to the carriage waiting to take them to the county gaol and law courts. Turning to face The Gatehouse he saw, at last, the unmistakable form of The Gaffer, standing, keys in hand as always, on the step of the prison doorway. A large man of about fifty, he had a kindly face, and waved benignly as the door of the wagon slammed shut and the wheels turned jerkily over the cobbles, taking William and the others away from St Albans, forever.

Chapter Twenty-Six

September 1800
Hertford

The day William had been dreading finally arrived.

Led in chains to a waiting cart he, and seventeen other prisoners, were making their final, miserable journey to the county court at which their fates would be decided by the jury, 'Twelve men and true', and the judge, who would determine whether they lived or died.

It was a short journey from the Ware Road gaol to Shire Hall where the assizes were to be conducted that day. All along the way crowds of local people stood and jeered, some throwing stale food, vegetables, or small stones at the unfortunate prisoners as they rattled slowly by. Immediately on leaving the gaol, the prisoners were taken past the gallows, erected just beyond the thick brick walls, a stark reminder of the final drop which awaited many in William's unfortunate circumstances.

None of the prisoners spoke, except to curse loudly the rabble who lined the road, taking cruel delight in their misfortune. This served only to add to the crowd's entertainment- a good day out after an hour or two drinking themselves senseless at one of the many local taverns. Inn keepers and tavern owners alike looked forward eagerly to the assizes and hoped for a good hanging or two to keep the crowds up and about, looking for food and drink to sustain them during the long day. William looked out from the back of the cart at the people who thronged the street. Who were they, and why could they not see the injustice which was so clear to William himself? Could they not understand that he, William Parker, was the *victim*, guilty only of defending himself in the face of a vicious attack by a spiteful and unfeeling assailant? Was there nobody out there able, or willing, to let the world know that there had been a huge and tragic mistake? Was he to swing for a crime of which he was not guilty? A stone struck him full on the shoulder waking him from his daydream, at which a cheer went up from a section of the crowd reminding him yet further that he was not amongst friends.

On reaching their destination the prisoners were pulled roughly off the cart and dragged, complaining, to the large cell in which they would be held until their turn came to appear before the court. Some wept and prayed, whilst others stared unblinking ahead, their minds lost in faraway thoughts known only to themselves and their Maker. One by one they were called: Jack Sheppard, 28 years old, habitual burglar. Guilty! Seven years' transportation to Botany Bay, Australia. James Hind, 34 year-old highwayman. Guilty! Sentenced to death by hanging. George Barrington aged 14 years, street-thief. Convicted of stealing a silver watch from a Miss Elizabeth Ironmonger, as she stood and looked in a shop window. Five years' hard labour. Mary Toft, aged about seventeen, hoaxer. Sentence: transportation to Botany Bay, fourteen years...and so it went on until William found himself entirely alone in the empty cell.

'William Parker!' came the abrupt call from along the passageway which led to the courtroom. The door swung open heavily, creaking upon its rusting hinges.

'On your feet, Parker! It's late and we all need to get 'ome to our 'ouses. The judge is ready to drop and the jury have 'ad their fun and want to join the rest of the mob in The Bell and Bull! Let's be 'aving you lad.'

At this, William made his way into the dark passage and walked slowly to the courtroom. As he entered the doorway, his hands still in chains, he was greeted by the sound of rough voices and the course laughter of those in the public gallery. It had been a good day and the prospect of another hanging had put the rabble into a joyous mood. Entering the room he shielded his eyes from the glare of the summer sunlight streaming through the windows opposite. Loud boos were heard from the gallery and a swooning woman cried, 'Oo would fink such a fine young man could do such a wicked fing!' before falling into a theatrical faint, much to the amusement of those surrounding her. Another screamed, 'Murderer! Murderer!' and had to be told to shut up or leave the court by the irascible judge who now desired nothing more than plate of lamb cutlets, kidney pies, and a lemon pudding all washed down with a tankard of best porter. He belched at the thought before gesturing impatiently at William to stand up straight in the dock. Not bothering with the formalities of asking the prisoner to confirm his identity he addressed him directly.

'Parker. William Parker. You have been accused of the wicked and heinous murder of...' he had to check his pile of notes to remember the details, 'a one Master Adam Thomas Clarke, late of High Trees in the village of Upper Hensford, in the county of Hertford. Do you understand the charge?'

William nodded that he did, and looked around the court in the empty hope of seeing a face that he recognised, a single friendly face who would tell the court the truth of what had happened at the lock as he lay dozing on the damp grass. How it had all been a big mistake and how he had risked his own life to save that of one who would have him dead. But instead, his eyes met the long cold stare of one whose only thought was to see him hang for the death of his eldest son: Mr Clarke, silver-topped cane in hand and dressed in black from head to toe, need say nothing to let William know that he was there for one reason and one reason only-to avenge his son's untimely death.

'And how do you plead? Guilty or not guilty?' slurred the judge, eyeing William with a face that was both bored and impatient.

'Not Guilty.' William's voice was barely audible over the noise from the gallery and he was told to repeat his plea, 'this time so as we all can hear it!'

The next half an hour was spent hearing Mr Clarke's lawyer extol the virtues of Adam. The court heard how Adam had been preparing to help his father run the family business, built up after many years of hard work and much investment into the local community of Hensford. They were told that Adam had been a loyal and hard-working young man, well-educated in the manners of the day, a talented horseman and a person of great promise. The jury were asked to consider the scene at the lock- the lock on the canal built by the dead boy's father who had, in his infinite generosity, given the accused's family the opportunity to make something better of themselves, even employing the father as his lock-keeper and accommodating them in a fine cottage in which they could live in comfort. And what was William Parker's response to this act of Christian generosity? To murder, in cold blood, the most loving son of his father's employer and benefactor! To murder him! And by what means? To drown him! To hold him down beneath the cold dark waters of the very canal, at the very lock, built by the esteemed Mr Clarke for the good of Hensford and its people! This was murder; and murder most foul!

And so it proceeded, with the public in the gallery alternately gasping and crying out at the account of how the dead body was discovered and hauled to the bank only to be recognised, not as any common labourer, but as the son and heir of Hensford's finest family.

The judge, meanwhile, struggled to stay fully awake and on more than one occasion nodded off, much to the amusement of the crowd and the frustration of the jury, whose patience was stretched to breaking point. It had been a long and tiring day, and they had had enough of murder and mayhem, and wanted no more than to return home to a hot meal and the bosom of their families. In their minds the young man in front of them was clearly guilty: a member of the poorer classes, consumed with jealousy of his wealthier and more fortunate victim, who took the opportunity to do the son of his employer to death. For what reason other than jealousy, only he would ever know. Besides, it was late and they wanted to go home before darkness descended, and the streets, already awash with drunks and cutpurses, got any more dangerous.

The judge's mind was all but made up when he asked if there was anyone there to speak on the boy's behalf.

William looked around the court once more but saw nobody he recognised. Tightening his grip on the bar he dropped his head and waited for the verdict he knew must come: Guilty-death by hanging! ...on the very gallows spied that morning from the back of the prisoners' cart.

As the judge reached for his black cap and made to open his mouth to pronounce the guilty verdict a shout went up from a corner of the gallery hidden to William. It was a voice he thought he knew but in his present, confused, state could not identify. Someone from the village? No- too well-spoken. Not the voice of a local man. Not the accent of one from the valley. But, nevertheless, someone familiar.

The judge craned his neck to see the form of a tall man of about forty years standing just within the courtroom, but hidden from William by the jostling crowd which still packed the public gallery.

'I have evidence the present court needs to hear, my Lord! This boy is innocent of the crime of which he is so unjustly accused!'

A gasp went up once more from the assembled gathering as Mr Clarke stood, amazed, his mouth silently forming the name of a man he believed he knew and trusted...

Adam's Lock

Chapter Twenty-Seven

Wednesday December 19th 2010
High Trees Conference Centre

David tugged hard on the handbrake and made sure the mini-bus was in gear before switching off and announcing they had arrived. The ageing vehicle strained forward as he got out and slid open the door, allowing the four children to follow him. As they emerged, a couple stretched their arms theatrically as if coming to the end of a day's hard drive rather than the five minutes it had taken from school to conference centre.

'Right. Grandma Dot said she'd be here at ten past one, so she should be along any minute now. Is your mum in the office today, Lee?' said David.

'No!' said Lee, a little too quickly. 'She's not here today. She's on a... training course, or something.' He searched for additional, supporting detail. 'Something to do with filing in the office. Important stuff. On the computer.'

'That's a shame. Would have been nice to say hello,' said David.

'Yeah,' said Lee, avoiding his teacher's gaze.

The sound of a car coming up the hill at speed made the children turn, just in time to see a pair of headlights rake the trees then dip to point directly towards them. They covered their eyes and then jumped back as a sports car, in racing green, roof down in spite of the cold, came to a noisy halt behind the school bus. The engine revved loudly once before guttering to a throaty stop.

'OMG, it's Grandma Dot!' said Kirsty, but by the time she'd said it the others were already circling the car, taking in the dark leather interior and stroking the sleek body as if it were an animal.

'Hello you lot, sorry I'm late. The old girl here is just like me and doesn't like the cold.'

'I say, Grandma Dot,' said David, a huge smile upon his face. 'A nineteen eighty…five Morgan 4/4 if I'm not very much mistaken! Parents had a Morgan before I was born,' he explained.

'Very good, Mr Stacey! Nearly right. Nineteen eight *three* actually. She's my baby. The love of my life.' She removed the goggles and headscarf she was wearing, un-noticed by the awestruck youngsters, and stuffed them into her bag.

The children took in the two circular spotlights mounted just above the gleaming silver bumper, and the elegant curve of the bull-nosed grille. They bent to touch the spokes of the wheels, running their fingers over them like the strings of small, circular harps. They peered into the mirrors, patted the spare wheel gently and touched the brown wooden steering wheel as if this was a craft from another world- which in some respects, it was.

'So you like her then, children.'

'That is *so* cool, Grandma Dot!' It was Lee who said what all the others, including David, were thinking. 'I mean it's...it's...' but words failed him and it was Kirsty who finally breathed an *'awesome'* at which everyone nodded their agreement.

Mesmerised by the beauty of the car, they were jolted from their reverie by the sound of their teacher's phone going off. Seeing that it was school calling, David moved off a little and left Grandma Dot to explain further the origins of the car, allowing the children, one by one, to sit in the driving seat.

'Sorry folks, there's a crisis at school which means I'm going to have to go back. Can't promise to get back in time to pick you up at the end of the visit, I'm afraid. You going to be all right do you think? Grandma Dot?' David looked a little anxious.

'No problem, Mr Stacey. I know it's not strictly, *ahem*, in line with school policy but I am a responsible adult and I'll make sure they don't come to any harm.'

'Great,' said David. 'Look, I tell you what. I'll get the school office to ring your parents and if there's any problem I'll make sure someone comes up to be with you. You've all got permission slips, haven't you? Okay, let's just do that then.'

He jumped back into the driver's seat and turned the key. The engine refused once, refused twice then kicked into action to the ironic cheers of the four children. David smiled and wiped his brow melodramatically before lowering the window and reminding the children to be good. He then crunched the gears and, giving the children a painful look, lurched out of the drive and down the hill.

'Well, that was exciting!' said Grandma Dot, before leading the group up the steps to the shelter of the portico that framed the front of the magnificent old building. Two huge black doors, adorned with a gleaming brass knocker and letterbox, gave onto a bright foyer and thence onto the large reception hall. Grandma Dot reminded them once again to be on their best behaviour, and to be very careful what they touched. 'It's a grand old house and full of important corporate types. I don't think we will constitute their usual 'clientele' somehow,' she said, before pushing at the glass door between them and the reception desk.

The five stood waiting while a smartly dressed young woman finished a phone conversation. The phone looked painfully jammed between her chin and her shoulder as she consulted a computer screen and jotted down details on a pad, 'High Trees Conference Centre', and a picture of the house, printed along its top edge. She looked up and mouthed 'one minute' before eventually wishing the caller the compliments of the season and putting the phone back on its cradle. She blew her cheeks out and smiled before asking what she could do to help. A shocked-looking Lee, who had been dreamingly admiring her red lips and long, dark hair, shuffled quickly to the left and indicated Grandma Dot who came to the front and introduced herself to the receptionist.

'Dorothy Huggins. Local historian and curator of the Adam's Lock Canal Museum.' She smiled and offered her hand which the receptionist took a little sheepishly.

'Glad to make your acquaintance...' the older woman strained to look over her glasses, '*Madeleine.*'

'And yours,' she replied. 'Now, how can I help you?'

Grandma Dot explained to Madeleine how they had an appointment with Mrs Armstrong at a half past one and, after checking her screen, the young woman directed them to sit on the large leather sofas next to the main door. 'I'll tell her that you're here and she'll be down shortly.' She smiled directly at Lee who blushed visibly and hung his head to look at his feet.

The children sat down taking in the sheer grandeur of the place. Nearby stood the biggest Christmas tree any of the children had ever seen. Over twenty feet tall, it filled its corner and almost touched the ceiling. It shimmered and gleamed with a thousand fairy lights which subtly changed their patterns every half minute or so.

But dominating, in the centre of the ceiling, hung a magnificent chandelier, the scale and beauty of which took even Grandma Dot's breath away. It was the size of a small room and owned the airy space with its loops and tassels that fell like crystal waterfalls high above their heads. Slight movements- a door opening- would send a myriad beads and prisms into a frenzy of flashes, glints and gleams: explosions and arrows of spellbinding light that did for the children what no video, no computer graphic or CGI, had ever done. They sat, like infants under a starlit sky, transfixed by the beauty and complexity of what they saw.

'OMG!' It was Kirsty again. 'This place is *amazing!*'

The others said nothing, just looked at the new world above their heads, with Lee stealing the odd glimpse of Madeleine, when he hoped nobody was looking.

Then Alex, scanning the hall, turned his attention to the pictures and portraits that adorned the walls. Landscapes and still-life paintings rubbed shoulders, almost literally, with paintings of the great and good: mainly august and severe, they appeared to look down with a benign contempt on those who sat staring back up at them. And one portrait in particular, placed high on the wall at the foot of the winding staircase, caught his eye and would not let it go. In it, a family posed against a backdrop of blue and what seemed to Alex to be the soft, rolling contours of the Chilterns. The gentleman looked directly at the viewer as did the lady and two children.

She sat on a beautiful chaise-longue whilst the man stood, proud and assured, one hand placed on the top of a silver-topped stick, the other on his hip. A baby, asleep on the woman's lap, and two boys, one standing, and a younger brother sitting at her feet, completed the family. He was sure that this was one of those paintings where the eyes would follow you around the room and he decided to check his theory at the earliest opportunity. As it happened this was not long in coming as a tall, elegantly dressed woman emerged from the back office, and approached the group.

'Mrs Huggins! How *lovely* to meet you!' She thrust a hand out confidently, nodding hellos to the four children.

'It's Miss, but please call me Dorothy,' she replied. 'And you must be Mrs Armstrong.'

'Indeed I am. Welcome to High Trees- now please, come with me.' Her smile was fixed, and did not include her eyes.

The group stood up and followed her to the office on the far side of the entrance hall. Men and women, some wearing fluffy white dressing gowns, wove their way towards a door marked 'Spa' whilst others tapped away furiously at their laptops, or simply sat and read the glossy magazines dotted around the glass-topped coffee tables.

As he walked, Alex glanced up at the portrait and was more convinced than ever that the eyes of family were indeed following him, and Lee shot a glance over at the desk, but Madeleine was not to be seen.

They entered Mrs Armstrong's office. 'Please, do sit down,' she said, joining them on a suite of easy chairs. 'Can I get anyone a drink?'

Grandma Dot spoke for the group, saying that they had all recently had lunch and that they were keen not to impose too much on their host's time.

'Well, I am a very busy woman,' she replied, glancing at her watch, 'and I do have a very important client to see at two fifteen. Now, how can I be of assistance?'

Grandma Dot detected a slight twitch in Mrs Armstrong's smile and suspected that time would be of the essence so, rather than asking the children to explain the reason for their being there, took the reins herself. Mrs Armstrong listened and was apologetic when asked directly about the history of the house.

'I'm not a local- I'm a Tring girl myself. But I do have to say that your name Alex, Clarke, seems to ring a bell. I think the Clarkes may have lived here a couple of hundred years ago. George the something I believe Miss Huggins- third or fourth was it?'

'Spot on I'd say,' nodded Grandma Dot. 'Could be either, or both, depending on exactly when we are talking about. We were rather wondering if we could have a look around the house, maybe have a look at some of the rooms, get a feel for the place?'

The centre manager looked uncomfortable and explained that this wasn't something head office normally recommended-especially in light of the children's ages.

'We'll be as good as gold,' Jo assured her, adding that she had never seen such a beautiful Christmas tree and how she, Mrs Armstrong, must have a great eye for decorations. Flattered, she told the girl that it was down to their man in Hampshire who came up every year then, relaxing, offered them a quick tour of the house.

'Thirty minutes mind- and please don't advertise the fact,' she said. A few moments later they stood at the foot of the grand staircase, then started to climb.

Alex glanced furtively at the portrait then quickly averted his own eyes as the family seemed to watch his every move. Lee too looked elsewhere and just caught a glimpse of a starched blue uniform before they turned a corner and were out of sight once more.

As they walked along the stylish corridors, adorned with a mixture of paintings, old and modern, Mrs Armstrong filled them in with what little she knew about the house. It was hundreds of years old, had fallen into disrepair and, in the early 1990's, had been bought by the present owners as an addition to their nationwide chain of conference centres. She knew that some old stables had been pulled down at the back and that the roof still leaked in places during heavy rainfall, something she asked them to keep to themselves. Although she was no expert, she was particularly pleased to tell them that a number of old paintings, including the imposing family portrait in the main entrance hall, had been discovered hidden, but perfectly preserved, beneath wooden panelling put up some time, she believed, in the sixties.

*

They finally arrived at the long top-corridor far away from the main business of the house with its conference rooms, lounges and spa. It was cold and unloved, the carpets threadbare, with traces of the original paintwork showing through the peeling wallpaper, which Grandma Dot estimated probably dated to the1920's or 30's.

'Well, that's just about it,' said Mrs Armstrong, unused to venturing so far from the comfort of her office. 'Not much up here of interest, I'm afraid, so nothing more to see or say about the place really. So, I hope you have enjoyed your visit and I'm sorry I wasn't able to be of more use. And now, if you'll excuse me, we have a group of *very* important guests arriving shortly and I am needed downstairs. It's been lovely meeting you all!'

The youngsters smiled weakly, resigned to the fact that they were leaving empty-handed, so to speak.

'Mrs Armstrong- what's behind that little door?' asked Grandma Dot, pointing towards a small hatch, barely visible in the weak light of the single bulb.

'Door?' asked the younger lady, readjusting her glasses to get a better look. 'Can't say I've ever noticed a *door* to be honest. Tend not to come up here much. An attic maybe? Something to do with a water-tank? I've really no idea.'

'Would you mind awfully if I took a peek, Mrs Armstrong? That's just me I'm afraid, a nosy old bird who just can't help sticking her beak into things!'

Mrs Armstrong looked slightly taken aback at the image, and glanced down again at her watch to signify that her precious time was now up and that she really had to be getting back to her desk.

'Look, if you are happy for me to stay with the children, I promise we won't wander. It would be fantastic if we could just spend another thirty minutes, no more than an hour, to make sure we haven't missed anything- before we go I mean. What do you say Mrs Armstrong? For the good of the children's education,' she wheedled.

Mrs Armstrong smoothed the cuff of her smart jacket over her watch and took in the bank of imploring looks.

'Well, if you put it like that, I suppose, it would do no harm to let you have a little time up here by yourselves. But you *must* promise not to stray from this corridor and be very careful rummaging around under the eaves- you know, health and safety and all that.'

'We promise!' smiled Grandma Dot, gripping her arm gently. 'We will spend no more time up here than we really have to, and we'll be out of your hair before your important guests arrive. Shall we say an hour?'

'Very well, but do be careful. It wouldn't do for anyone to get hurt.'

'We promise!' said Lee, for the rest of the group, and they stood in silence until the manager had turned the corner and they heard the soft slam of the door at the foot of the staircase leading to the landing below.

'Yessss!' said Kirsty and punched the air. 'Now, this is what I call *real* history hunting. An old house with a mysterious hidden door leading into an unexplored attic! It doesn't get much better that this!'

'Steady on Kirsty,' cautioned the old lady. 'Don't forget what that nice Mrs Armstrong said about being careful, and you really mustn't get over-excited. We might just get to see a rusty old water-tank, complete with dead pigeon, or find out how many spiders share the place with all the *important* guests- and *the spiders* get to use the spa for free!'

The children sniggered before Alex pointed out that they really needed to explore while they still had time.

Grandma Dot took the lead as they walked to the under-sized door, barely visible through the gloom. She ran her fingers around the frame and pushed at the door gently to establish if it was stuck, painted-in over the years. The panel shifted slightly under pressure, but it was clear that no-one had been through that doorway for a very long time. Grandma Dot's hand closed on the small brass handle and pressed down firmly. Nothing. The mechanism was stuck, rusted from years of under-use and neglect. The old lady tried again in vain and stepped back with a heavy sigh.

'It's no good, I can't shift the thing. Mind you, these old hands aren't what they used to be. What about you, Lee? If you can land a five-pound pike I expect you can force a rusty old lock.'

Lee stepped forward, a wide grin on his face, proud to have been chosen at this critical point in their adventure.

'Well, my dad *is* a'

'master-locksmith, yeah we know,' said Alex with an edge to his voice, 'and my dad's an Olympic power weight-lifter.'

'No he's not-he's an accountant,' said Jo.

'An *actuary*, actually' corrected Alex tartly.'

'What's one of those then, when it's at home?'

'Um… a sort of accountant, I think,' replied Alex, and looked at the floor.

'Look, children,' interrupted Grandma Dot, 'let's not start arguing. Not at this exciting moment!' Alex looked abashed as Lee stepped forward and tried the handle. Nothing, again. The old house was not ready to give up its secrets that easily if, indeed, it had anything to hide in the first place.

'I've got something here that might help,' said Lee producing a many-bladed knife from an inside pocket. The other children gasped and Kirsty warned him that if the local policeman saw him he'd have him arrested or given an Asbo or something.

'No chance,' Lee replied with a grin, 'he goes fishing with my dad and knows exactly what I use this for! And anyway, do you want me to open the door or not?'

With that, the tip of his tongue flicking with concentration, Lee started to work upon the area around the lock. Bits of old paint cracked off the woodwork and slowly, slowly, the door appeared to loosen and give slightly to a firm push of his hand. For what seemed an eternity, Lee picked away carefully at the painted-in hinges, working his way around the gap between door and frame, before he tapped downwards smartly on the ornate handle. With a crack, the handle moved from the horizontal, to point towards the carpet. The children gasped again and jumped as the door popped open an inch or two to reveal...nothing. Nothing but the black emptiness of a cold space between wall and roof tiles; here and there, tiny points of light piercing the void.

'Well *done*, Lee!' exclaimed Grandma Dot, and gestured to him to allow her to take a closer look. Her head and shoulders disappeared from view.

'It's very dark,' her muffled voice echoed, stating the obvious. 'I can't see a thing.'

The children looked at each other, frustrated and excited at one and the same time.

'Jo, my dear, pass me my handbag will you? Lovely. Can you get out my iPhone so I can use the torch app, there's a good girl.'

Jo grabbed the bag and gingerly rummaged through its contents. It didn't seem right, somehow, going through the old lady's things. Eventually, beneath the make-up and the sweets (and was that a pair of goggles and a pouch of *pipe-tobacco*?) she located the phone, and passed it to Grandma Dot who immediately switched on the light.

'Aha!' exclaimed the old lady whose voice was immediately drowned out by a chorus demanding to know what it was that she had seen, what the 'aha!' signified, and could *they* have a look.

'Keep calm everyone,' she said when things had died down sufficiently to make her voice heard. 'There's a very small space indeed, maybe only a foot or two high, and certainly not big enough for this old history detective to get into without being stuck for evermore.'

'I'll go,' said Kirsty, who would have been considered small even for a girl three years younger. 'I can fit into *tiny* spaces. Dad calls me 'Mouse' at home and I always used to win Hide and Seek at Christmas.'

'Well, I'm not sure dear. As the lady says, we have to be careful about health and safety. Can't have you getting stuck and never going to university, can we? How would I explain that to your poor mother?'

'Grandma Dot, please! I went caving once with the scouts. It was well-good, and I was one of the best. Got a badge I think. Please Grandma Dot, it's too exciting just to close the door and go away again!'

The others joined in and eventually (and without much real effort needed on their part) the old lady gave in to their pleading. 'Oh, very well,' she said brushing the cobwebs from her hair and handing the phone to Kirsty.

Wriggling carefully over the small step, and into the tight space, she turned to the right, crawling on all fours until only the soles of her shoes, complete with price sticker, were all that could be seen in the flickering torchlight.

'What can you see?' asked the children, but their words evaporated into the cold, dark air of the eaves, and they had to make do with following the shuffling noises as she made her way further and further from the doorway.

'Be careful, my dear,' reminded Grandma Dot as she fiddled nervously with the strap of her handbag. 'Don't venture too far and for goodness sake don't get yourself stuck!'

Minutes passed. The sound of a body moving on the other side of the thin wall told them that Kirsty was making her way back to the entrance. Suddenly, the trainers, and then a dusty face, appeared at the hole to be met with a barrage of questions and demands.

Grandma Dot assumed command before gently asking 'the mouse' what, if anything, she had seen. Much to everyone's intense disappointment, she told them that she had found nothing beyond a few rags and a lot of water pipes. A hole in the roof had allowed her to see her house in the distant village, but that was it. Nothing more to report. The children's heads dropped as they knew their time was running out.

'I can try that way now, Grandma Dot,' beamed Kirsty as she turned awkwardly and started to make her way to the left. See you in a minute.'

'We haven't much time left Kirsty,' the old woman reminded her. 'Mrs Armstrong is expecting very important guests and we did promise her...' but before she could finish her sentence the feet had disappeared again.

Minutes passed, and the children were starting to think of the long walk home, and of polite tea-time conversations with their families who would say things like 'Never mind dear, you did your best,' and, 'I hope you said thank-you to Grandma Dot and to the nice lady who showed you round.' Lee fiddled with his knife and Alex pretended to knock cricket balls back along the narrow corridor, past an imaginary bowler, and out through the roof.

Suddenly, the silence was shattered by the excited squeaks of Kirsty scurrying her way back towards the doorway.

'Grandma Dot! Grandma Dot! Come quickly, I think I've found something!'

'I can't come anywhere dear and neither can anyone else. It's too small a space! What is it you've found?'

Kirsty appeared panting at the doorway and took a deep breath so she could speak. In her hand she held a dirty white wig, like a judge's wig, thought Alex, and a piece of embroidered material, like a handkerchief, or a necktie perhaps.

'I got these!' she said, thrusting her hand towards Grandma Dot, while the others looked on, eyes open wide.

'Well. I think we can safely say that these were not bought in Marks and Spencer's!' said Grandma Dot, bringing them closer to her face so that she could study them more easily. 'Georgian, late eighteenth or early nineteenth century I would say. Beautiful needlework on this, and the wig is typical of what gentlemen would have worn, especially older ones or those with a bit of money! Good girl! 'Mouse' indeed- more like a squirrel finding a store of hidden goodies.'

'There's more Grandma Dot-lots more stuff! Mainly clothes and things and there's a box, but it's too heavy for me and I can't budge it.'

'A box? Let me have a go- I can crawl along there, I know I can!' It was Lee again, his excitement threatening to do him physical injury.

'Are you sure you can fit in there, Lee?' asked Grandma Dot, 'aren't you a bit on the big side for caving?'

'No way,' he protested, and ushered Kirsty out of the way, grabbing the phone as he went. 'How far is it?' came a little voice a few seconds later, to which Kirsty replied that it was about a minute's crawl round the corner.

After what seemed like an age, Lee could be heard as he crawled backwards towards the opening. He eventually appeared, his hands empty apart from several lengths of fishing line which he handed to Alex. He was breathing heavily and sweat glistened on his brow.

'Managed to drag the box a little but got sort of stuck...decided to tie some of this to the little handles on the ends... wrapped the rest around the middle.' He gulped in a deep breath and mopped his forehead with his sleeve.

'Is there anything you don't have in that jacket of yours?' asked Alex, genuinely impressed.

'Yeah- a flat screen TV,' said his friend almost shyly. 'Anyway, wait until I get back to the box and then pull. Together we should be able to get it to here.' He quickly disappeared from sight again, but could still be heard through the thin wall, making steady progress along the narrow passageway.

A minute or so elapsed before they heard his voice saying loudly and clearly, 'On-three - start -to -pull -steadily –on- the –lines...understood?'

'Understood!' shouted Alex, and waited with the others for his instructions.

'One. Two. Three...' then a thump and a cry echoed round the space.

'Are you alright, Lee?' Grandma Dot asked. 'You're not hurt are you?'

'No. Everything's fine. Just bumped my head a bit trying to get the box into position. Not much space! Give it another tug and I'll be more careful this time.'

Over the next few minutes the children, encouraged by Grandma Dot, pulled at the fishing line, edging the box slowly towards the entrance. Lee's trainers were the first things to come into sight, followed by his legs and then the green of his blazer. Eventually, Lee half-emerged from the hole, exhausted and gasping for air, a corner of the old box tantalizingly close to seeing daylight for the first time in over two hundred years.

'Easy, Lee, be careful not to strain yourself. Let the rest of us do this last bit for you. Careful with your head on the door frame, love!' Grandma Dot fussed, her voice uncharacteristically shaky with excitement and anticipation.

Lee flopped onto the carpet, allowing the others to guide the heavy wooden box-more of a chest than a box- to the very edge of the doorway. 'Right! Time for real team-work to get this time-capsule safely into the twenty-first century!' said Grandma Dot , who organised the remaining children so they could each take a corner and, on her instruction, lift the box the few inches down onto the carpeted floor of the corridor.

It sat, unmoving, about the size of a large printer box. Lee brought out his knife once more and, selecting an appropriate blade, carefully cut away the nylon line. The children could barely breathe and nobody spoke. They knelt and stared at the box as if it were the very death mask of King Tutankhamen, or a treasure-chest lifted from the rotting hulk of a pirate ship.

It was Grandma Dot, the undisputed captain, who spoke first.

'Well, it *is* undoubtedly old. It's made from a dark wood- probably mahogany -and could be a tea-chest or something similar. Very popular in the late eighteenth century when tea was expensive, you see. But I don't know,' she said shaking her head a little, 'I'm not an expert on these things.'

She took out a tissue and started to gently wipe away some of the grime and dust of two centuries. Still nobody dared breathe. Slowly, illuminated by the waning light of two mobile phones, minute details started to appear through the gloom: what appeared to be a small fan, carved from lighter wood, decorating the lid; the edge of a silver shield; a small key-hole inlayed in creamy white ivory, all gradually took shape before their widening eyes. The old lady, by this time breathing hard herself, worked on the shield with gentle sweeping movements until, bit by tiny bit, more details gradually emerged. She stopped to compose herself, and slowly cleaned her glasses before resuming her delicate task.

The silver shield was dirty and black from age, but was unmistakably adorned with finely-carved details. The first to emerge was an elaborate capital letter 'A', the legs swirling and long. The next, occupying the middle of the shield and separated from its neighbour by a simple full-stop, appeared to be an F, or possibly an E, it was difficult to be absolutely sure. To the right of the shield's centre was the third and final letter, unmistakably a capital 'C'.

The children looked at Grandma Dot who stopped, and put down her tissue.

'This, children, belonged to someone with the initials A, F (or possibly E), C.'

'Could it be a C for 'Clarke'?' thought Alex, remembering what Mrs Armstrong had said to him earlier that afternoon-but he just could not bring himself to say it out loud.

'It's locked, which suggests it contains something, or some things, of worth. Of value to the person or persons who once possessed it, at least. But it is firmly locked and, as there does not appear to be a key, presents us with an annoying and frustrating problem: we cannot look inside!'

A groan went round the group who took the opportunity to break the silent tension that had so affected them over the previous few minutes. How many minutes, no-body had any idea as time had appeared to stand still, and the world around them disappear, to be replaced only by an ancient wooden box viewed in the dim light of the latest handheld electrical gadgets.

'But we can't just leave it like that Grandma Dot!' moaned Alex. 'You know, 'Oh well, that's it then. Now what's for tea?' '

'No, he's right' added Kirsty. I'll go bonkers if we can't look inside. It's like something out of Dr Who or Raiders of the Lost Ark, or something. We've just *got* to open the box!'

Lee had by this time regained his breath and said, very quietly, 'My dad's a master-locksmith and', he looked around daring anyone to interrupt him this time, 'I know how to pick locks, to open them without a key...'

Once again, silence fell upon the group, and Grandma Dot stood back to let the new hero take centre-stage. Lee, yet another blade selected from this magic knife of his, worked quietly with a patience known only to fishermen. Using a small, spike-like, blade he gently angled the point this way then that, listening carefully for any tell-tale clicks to guide him in his task. Perspiration beaded on his forehead despite the fact that the corridor in which they were gathered was cool; again, nobody dared breathe.

A sudden, final click, and a slight shifting of the lid signalled his task was over. An audible out-breath was followed by a cheer, and hugs all round, before the children realised who they were embracing and drew back, embarrassed.

'Lee! You've only gone and done it!' somebody cried, and everyone fell about laughing with the relief.

It was some minutes before Grandma Dot was able to re-establish calm and explained to the children what they were going to do next.

'Could I use that amazing implement of yours, Lee dear?' she beamed, and selected a short, stubby blade more like a screwdriver than a knife. Tenderly almost, she moved the blade around the edge of the lid, prising it gently away from the main part of the box to which it had become partially stuck. Despite her excitement, she was careful to respect the beauty of the box and the time and effort put in by its maker so many years before.

Chapter Twenty-Eight

June 1801
Botany Bay, New South Wales - Australia

William awoke, still a prisoner; still alive. The air was warm and damp, and flies buzzed in a suffocating swarm around his face. He reeked of sweat, and was unwashed and horribly dishevelled, his matted hair reaching below his shoulders. Through a small porthole he could hear distant shouting, and from above the sound of birds calling to each other-screeching cries that were loud, foreign, and unfamiliar. His bones ached and his torn flesh hurt from the rough wooden boards on which he had lain for what seemed like an eternity. Through the grey, below-decks light, he could just make out the dark shapes of his fellow travellers as they too awoke. Someone cleared their throat and spat whilst another cursed the birds for waking him from his slumber.

William stretched and felt the room sway gently from side to side, up and down, to and fro. Lifting himself painfully onto his elbow, and careful not to wake the man shackled to his leg, he scratched and slapped at the lice to which his aching body had become a permanent host. Then he lay back and listened again to the sounds of the birds as they argued noisily overhead: raucous, but free.

Free? William was not.

But he *was* still alive.

Chapter Twenty-Nine

Wednesday December 19th 2010
Under the Eaves - High Trees Conference Centre

As Grandma Dot gazed at the small chest her mind drifted back to her childhood. To boxes of all sorts: colourful boxes tied up with scarlet ribbons, egg-boxes and apple-boxes, boxes for hats and boxes for shoes. Tissue boxes, and boxes of chocolates. And then, she thought, there is the box in which we are laid to rest: within which we end our days. Heavy and solid, borne gently aloft on six strong shoulders, they protect us from the cold damp earth of our final resting place.

'Grandma Dot? Are you alright? Grandma Dot?'

The old lady looked about her vacantly at the four faces, staring, the concern in their eyes clear for her to see.

'Oh, I'm so sorry m' dears, I'm fine. I must have drifted off. Now then, let's have a look at what this beautiful and mysterious box might contain.'

The children craned their necks to see what secrets the box held, what it might tell them about Hensford and its distant past. The scene was almost biblical, like the wise men at the crib. On this occasion, however, the gifts were for the visitors: visitors who had themselves travelled, in what felt like a miraculous way, across the span of time, in search of answers to all-important questions of their own.

Slowly, and to the creak of rusty hinges, the lid lifted. To their great relief the five treasure hunters saw that the box was not empty, but even with the help of torches it was difficult to make out the details of what it actually contained. Grandma Dot put her hand in and gently lifted out the first object -the first time it had moved in many generations. It glistened dully in the gloom- an edge here, a face there, catching the weakening glow of a child's phone.

'It's a mug of some sort. Silver I think. Maybe a christening mug?'

It was the size of a small cup with a curved handle formed into a fancy shape. Just visible was a series of intricate patterns engraved around the foot and rim –flowers, birds, the sun and moon. Grandma Dot took out another tissue and gently worked away at a central panel to reveal the faint outline of letters and numbers, as yet unreadable.

'Bring the light nearer will you Alex dear, there's a good boy', Grandma Dot said quietly, like the way you spoke in church.

Slowly, the letters and numbers began to reveal their secrets: 'Adam-Edmund-Clarke-Born- April 16th - AD 1783'. Alex gasped and put his hand to his mouth, suddenly barely able to breathe.

'It's a Clarke! It's a Clarke! Oh my God! It *is* a Clarke!'

Grandma Dot laid the silver mug carefully to one side but said nothing as she dipped her hand once more into the box. The children sat spellbound and in silence, and Jo put her arm around Alex who was clearly still suffering from the shock of the first revelation.

What emerged next was a long piece of material, about the size and shape of a tie or a scarf. Even in the poor light it was clearly made of an expensive cloth and had, in better days, been a vivid bright yellow. It was partly ripped and had been badly stained, but whether this was before or after it had been placed in the box was impossible to say.

'I'd say this was a neckerchief- a sort of light scarf worn neatly around here, by the throat-most probably belonging to Adam. Far too big for a baby so maybe something he wore as a young man. The dates sort of work, too. Silk neckerchiefs were very fashionable in Georgian times- he would have been about sixteen or seventeen at the turn of the century.'

Still the children said nothing. They sat mesmerised by what was unfolding in front of them. Never-not in a million years- had history lessons been like this. This was treasure to be sure. Not gold nor diamonds, but treasure all the same.

Next came a small silver ring, engraved with the same AEC initials, and a gold pin of the sort used to hold a tie or similar in place.

Low down in the box, and hidden until now, was a short riding crop and a pair of gloves made of the same good quality leather.

'Adam came from a wealthy family', said Grandma Dot, quietly. 'From the look of these items he was a smallish man, perhaps still a boy when these things were put in this box. How *fascinating*. A real-life detective story!'

She continued to delve deeper and brought out a small silver snuff-box, a quill and a finely-drawn but child-like sketch of a muscular horse pulling a hay-wagon.

Finally, her hand found what felt to her like a folded up wad of paper, about the size of a small book. Lifting it very carefully, clear of the box, she saw immediately what it was: a newspaper, tightly folded, and bound with a piece of fraying black ribbon. The ribbon was a little fragile, but the paper seemed to be in good condition given its probable age.

She gestured to the children to move back a little so that she could unpick the bow and lay the paper flat on the floor. The children watched intently as she gently unfolded and flattened the paper on the landing floor, then laid the ribbon to one side. Grandma Dot struggled to make out the print and asked

Alex, a good reader, to help her in the next task. He shuffled his way around the group to join her at her side and held his phone close.

'It's the Hertford Mercury! December 1800. Wow! Over two hundred years old and still in one piece!'

He searched the densely printed page for something to relay back to the group who were waiting silently for any morsel of news-anything at all about Adam or his family. Running his finger lightly over the page he read: 'Several cattle were drowned in the river Ver at the height of the latest floods to afflict St Albans...a girl was clubbed to death in the woods, murdered by her uncle...His Majesty King George is due to visit Hertford in the summer...' he mumbled, almost to himself, and then stopped, his finger hovering at a point somewhere near the bottom of the page. He raised his head and looked at the rest of the group, his eyes wide with disbelief. 'I think I've found something. I think I've found what we've been looking for!'

Then he paused. 'Grandma Dot, can *you* read it please?'

Grandma Dot took the paper in her hands, readjusted her glasses and slowly started to read:

Hertford Court- Assizes December 10th 1800

Dramatic End to Clarke Drowning Murder Trial!

The long awaited trial of William Parker, fourteen years old, formerly of The Lock-keeper's Cottage, Hensford, in the county of Hertford, has ended in high drama at Hertford Assizes. Accused of the murder, by drowning, of Adam Clarke, son of Mr Edmund Clarke Esq. and heir to the High Trees estate, Parker had spent several months awaiting trial in The Gatehouse St Albans, and since September of this year, at His Majesty's pleasure at Ware Street Gaol, Hertford.

The murder took place at a spot not a stone's throw from Parker's cottage where his father was, until the drowning, lock-keeper on the newly constructed Hensford Arm of which the victim's father was builder and owner. The Hensford Arm was opened only last summer to great acclaim providing swift transportation of high-quality building stone to London and Birmingham from the village quarry, also owned by Mr Clarke senior.

Parker was brought up from the cells to a packed courtroom, the last of twenty felons to be tried in a long day for the judge, Mr Justice Samuels, and the members of the jury. The day was warm and sunshine streamed through the windows causing the accused on more than one occasion to shield his eyes when addressing the court. The evidence against Parker was incontestable ['you couldn't argue with it', explained Grandma Dot] *and the jury took only eight minutes to find the wretch guilty of murder most foul. Several prisoners had been sent to the gallows earlier in the day and it seemed a foregone conclusion that the same fate awaited this sorry young man. As Justice Samuels reached for his black cap and members of the public started to move towards the exit, the peace of the courtroom was shattered by a voice from the gallery which dramatically halted the proceedings! Grown men looked aghast and several women swooned with the shock of it as a tall, well-dressed man of about forty years, addressed the court thus: 'Stop! My Lord. I have crucial evidence that the court needs to hear! This boy is innocent of the crime of which he is so unjustly accused!'*

Mr Justice Samuels, himself appearing shocked, demanded the man identify himself or risk being held in contempt of court.

'My name is John Saunders m'Lord. Forty three years of age and footman to Mr Clarke of High Trees, Hensford.'

275

A roar erupted from the gallery as a furious Mr Clarke stood to his feet waving a silver-topped stick and heaping insults of a most indelicate kind upon his once most-trusted employee.

The judge demanded Order in the Court and instructed Mr Clarke to sit down immediately or be removed from the Courtroom at once. This he did and sat scowling at the tall figure of Saunders now brought to the Witness Stand so all could see him and hear his Testimony.

Leaning forward and speaking in a quiet but composed voice the footman described how he had accompanied Adam, the deceased, to a point on the Canal not far from the Parkers' cottage. He had been instructed, he explained, to ride with Adam on a mission to 'teach the canal-boy a lesson in manners that he would not forget.' Asked to explain further, Saunders described an incident some months earlier in which William had saved Adam, Adam's father and the Lock-Keeper from certain death at the hands of a murderous Highwayman. In doing so, he, William, had made Adam appear a fool and a coward-'something Adam was unwilling to forgive or forget.'

A hushed courtroom heard how Clarke had found Parker dozing on the bank of the canal. Waiting with the horses, Mr.Saunders was unable to hear the exact words which passed between the two, but reported hearing raised voices and seeing 'Adam attack the younger boy, striking him several times forcibly about the face with a riding crop.' He told how was able to hear Parker cry out and saw both young men tumble into the water. He was unable to say with any certainty what had been the cause of the fall but believed the couple had grappled and slipped off the bank together.

At this point Mr Clarke senior was heard to shout 'Liar! Liar! The boy's a murderer-my only son's blood upon his hands! And you Saunders are finished- as good as dead!' On the judge's instruction he was then forcibly removed from the court, protesting loudly as he was dragged away.

Mr Saunders' testimony concluded as follows:

'I swear by almighty God that I then saw William surface, his face turned a deathly shade. I heard him shout 'Adam! Adam, where are you?' before plunging once more under the water in

search, I do honestly believe, of his assailant. He may have tried once more, I cannot be sure for I was in a state of high anxiety and, much to my shame my Lord, turned both horses and sped for home. And that is as much as I can tell the court.'

And with that John Saunders sat and wept, his hands pressed hard into his face, and could not be comforted as he was led from the stand.

Justice Samuels then ordered a ten-minute recess during which he would take some time to reconsider the case in light of the new evidence presented to him in this dramatic and most unexpected manner.

On returning, the judge demanded silence from a boisterous courthouse before ordering Parker to stand for sentencing. Parker did as he was instructed and tightly gripped the bar of the dock, his head bowed as he waited for the inevitable 'Guilty! Death by hanging!' to be pronounced.

The judge looked gravely at the accused, adjusting his spectacles for the final time that day.

278

'William Parker. You stand accused of the heinous crime of murder. It has been alleged that you did, on the 16th day of March 1800, cause Adam Clarke, a young man with a bright future, and heir to the his family fortune, to lose his life by drowning and that it was whilst in the grip of your hands that he breathed his last.'

Parker was seen to sway a little and grip the bar more tightly.

'I think there was little doubt that the unfortunate victim died beneath the waters of his father's own canal, whilst you, William Parker kicked, punched and otherwise fought him to the death. And for this you must ask your maker to show you mercy when eventually you face Him, as face Him you must. However, I am satisfied that you are of previous good character and earlier submissions by the Reverend Thompson of St James' Church, Hensford confirm this to be the case. I am also moved greatly by the powerful testimony of Mr Saunders here, an employee of the victim's father and not one I would normally expect to support the defence's side in such a case. As a consequence, I have decided NOT to administer the sentence of death by hanging but instead sentence you to fourteen years' *deportation to the penal colony in Port Jackson on the island of Australia. Sergeant, take him down!'*

And with that, the boy was taken away and out of the sight of the court which emptied onto the streets and into the inns, undoubtedly to discuss the events of this day, well into the small hours of the one which followed.

Rare it is when a convicted murderer escapes the noose in such dramatic and emotional circumstances, and one would hope that Mr Justice Samuels himself can look HIS Maker in the eye when he meets Him; as meet Him he must!'

Grandma Dot gently folded the paper and laid it back on the carpet, then took off her glasses and let them hang from the chain around her neck. Nobody said a thing for a while as they took in what the article was telling them. Eventually, it was Lee who broke the silence.

'So,' he said slowly, 'there was a murder, I mean a death, here in Hensford, two hundred years ago. Adam Clarke,' he looked at Alex, 'drowned near the lock. Adam's Lock. He dies 'cos he had a fight with William, William Parker. He was about our age. But William,' he added, 'was only defending himself and tried to get him out of the water even though he hated him.

So, is this what it's all about? Is this what started the Uppers and Lowers thing? It was William Parker. And Adam Clarke?'

Grandma Dot smiled gently and gave his shoulders a hug. 'Looks like it doesn't it? Two young men have a fight because one has made the other one look a fool. What would you youngsters say today? He was 'dissing' him? It goes too far, and only one lives to tell the tale. It's a tragedy. Nothing much changes does it?'

Jo wiped a small tear from the corner of her eye and looked away, a little embarrassed at how she was feeling over an incident that had played out so many years ago.

'That's so sad,' she said, 'and really, *two* boys lost their lives that day. Adam lost *his* under the water of the canal, and William lost his too, a long time later on the other side of the world. I wonder if he made it, or died on the ship before he even got there? I saw something on the TV once, about convicts in Australia, and it was horrible.'

'Well, we may never know dear,' said the old woman, 'but what we do know is that he was at least spared the hangman's noose and was given another chance of life, even if it *was* ten thousand miles away in the harsh new world of an Australian prison colony.'

The chime of the church clock down in the valley bottom reminded Grandma Dot of the time and she told the children that they really must be going. She carefully packed everything back in the wooden chest and asked Alex and Lee if they would very much mind carrying it downstairs for her. She would ask Mrs Armstrong if it would be all right for them to take everything back to the museum where she would ask local historians, much more expert than her, to study the contents in greater detail.

As the boys, one Upper, one Lower, carried the box carefully towards the car, the group talked further about what they had discovered. If this *was* what had split the village and had created the rift in the community, surely people on hearing the tale would realise that here was an ancient ghost that should now be laid to rest? Surely, the two groups could see it for what it was: a tragic mistake, which anyway happened ages ago, in which there were no winners - only losers on both sides. Why, two hundred or more years later, should they still be paying the price of a sad event now lost in the mists of time?

*

A mobile rang in a bag in Charles's office. David put down his glass and rummaged about, extraditing it from the mass of cards and papers- it was Grandma Dot. Charles and Mary lowered their voices as David strained to hear above the carols coming from an old CD player in the corner, until one of them noticed and turned the volume down low.

'Yes, non-stop Bing Crosby and Slade for the next few days, Grandma Dot. Anyhow, how did *you* get on?'

David listened quietly, interjecting with an occasional *aha* or *ooh* until the old lady reached the part where the painted-in door snapped open. He sat down and took a sip of his wine.

'What happened?' mouthed Mary, evidently now succumbing to the effects of whatever it was she had been drinking since the end of the school day.

David put up his hand and continued to listen, saying very little, much to the frustration of his two colleagues.

Then suddenly he stood up, oblivious to the glass of wine which then deposited its contents onto the carpet.

'That's *amazing* Dot!' he said. 'What did the kids think?' And then, 'fantastic result, and thank-you for everything you've done! Bye. See you soon.'

He sat again, flopping down on the chair, a wide grin threatening to cleave his face in two.

'David! You have to tell us wha's goin' on!' Mary sat on the arm of his chair. 'C'mon, spill the Christmas beans!' she slurred.

David took a deep breath.

'Well, firstly, thanks for the 'crisis phone-call' Charles. Worked a treat, and the kids were able to get on with things without looking to me for guidance all the time. Great- and Grandma Dot did a sterling job too. Without your...'

'Yeah, yeah, yeah Dave! Don't be boring. Cut to the chase! Tell us what was *amazing*, what was *fantastic*!'

Mary struggled to stay sitting on the arm of the chair, and gave David a little punch in the arm for emphasis.

'Right. They found a box- a sort of little chest with *loads* of stuff in -bits of clothing, a riding crop and, most amazing, most fantastic...' he did a drum roll on his knee, 'a newspaper article from 1800 that might explain the whole Uppers and Lowers thing! How about that!'

Charles came across the room and clapped his hand on David's shoulder.

'Well done, ol' buddy. That's truly amazing. Should be proud of yourself.'

'Flippin' brilliant Dave,' added Mary leaning in, depositing a kiss of red lipstick that would remain on his cheek till Christmas.

Chapter Thirty

Friday December 21st 2010
Outside the Graveyard - Our Lady's Church

School had closed early, the final day of a long term, and the two boys sat on the low wall of the graveyard. A strange, even suspicious place to sit, an observer might think, but for Alex and Lee this place felt right, a sort of spiritual nexus where the important places and events of the past six months appeared to come together, naturally: the lock, the quarry, the old cottages and now, Mr Richard's grave, all within a stone's throw of where they sat and talked. And, beyond the silhouette of St James's, you could just make out the Christmas lights of High Trees, twinkling like stars.

Across the canal, the sounds and sights of the Christmas Market intruded upon their discussion.

'Have you heard of ley-lines, Lee?'

'Nah. Are they a sort of optical illusion, or something?'

'No, not really. They're kind of lines across the countryside-no, not *across* the countryside, sort of *in* the countryside. No, they're invisible...it's really hard to explain.' Alex fell quiet.

'Why did you mention them then?' said Lee, his own face barely visible to Alex.

Where they sat an ancient Yew tree had left a section of wall bulging, ready to spill onto the path. Alex picked at the mortar, and weighed a morsel in his palm before tossing it into the grass.

'Don't know really. It's just that where ley-lines cross, there's supposed to be some special force, like magic, that makes things happen. A lot's happened here, hasn't it Lee?'

'You're not wrong,' said Lee. 'Bit spooky really. Can we go and sit somewhere else, now?'

They crossed the canal at the lock, careful not to slip as they negotiated the narrow walkway on top of the gates. The water trickled through the sluices, adding a seasonal tinkling to the noises of the market and the tiny, hastily-erected funfair.

'When I was kid I used to *love* that fair!' said Lee. 'It was *massive* then. What's happened to it?'

The pair pushed their way through the throngs of people vying to get the best bargains, or desperate to purchase all those things they had forgotten in the run-up to Christmas. The smells of hog-roast and mulled wine mixed with those of chestnuts and candy-floss, and on the corner, next to a festive-looking Feathers, children waited impatiently to see this year's incarnation of the man in red.

They shared a toffee-apple, and sat again on the steps of the village war memorial.

'So what you doing for Christmas, Lee?'

'Same as last year. Drinks at my aunty's-open presents- dinner at ours- big fat turkey- watch the Queen- more drinks-walk by the canal-home-telly-bed,' he reeled off the list without taking a breath. 'What about you, Alex?'

'Christmas day at my place, then pack on Boxing Day for France. I think we fly early the next morning. Can't remember. Then back, just after New Year.'

'Then-back-to-school!' they chanted, and laughed, in unison.

'I'd better be going Lee,' said Alex, and stood to go. Lee got up and looked over towards his house. A light was in the top window, which usually meant his mum was home from work.

'Yeah, same Alex,' he said.

'Just before you go,' said Alex, 'I got you this.'

He pushed a crumpled envelope into Lee's hand, embarrassed.

'Happy Christmas.'

'Oh, yeah,' his friend replied, looking down. 'Listen, sorry; I haven't got you one.'

'No worries,' said Alex.

The two gave each other an awkward hug, then Lee hurried away towards the safety of the crowd.

'And Alex!' he shouted over his shoulder, 'see you in January.'

He did not look back.

The End

Preview of:
'The Land Beyond the Seas'

The Sequel to Adam's Lock

Chapter One
Christmas 1803. Near Port Jackson, New South Wales.

Face down, in the hot, red, soil of Australia, the pain of the boot pressing down on his neck was excruciating, and the sand filling his mouth made breathing almost impossible. But what hurt William most was not the physical pain, the stabbing pressure of the heel on his spine. What wounded him, and what threatened to tear his heart out, was the indignity of it all. How could one man do this to another?

'On your knees prisoner Parker,' said the man in the uniform. 'And don't go trying any funny business or I'll be forced to use this,' he added, hefting the musket he was carrying so it pointed directly at the boy's head. William coughed, spat the sand back into the earth, and turned to look at his captor. A trickle of blood ran from his forehead causing him, in a real sense, to see red. He straightened up slowly, hands aloft, knowing that any attempt at escape would be futile and that any sudden movement could be his last.

The man backed off a couple of paces and gestured to William that he should move towards a rough canvas bag lying on the ground a few feet from where he was standing-the loop of a rope poked out of the opening at the top. A little way off, a horse neighed and pawed at the dry earth, impatient to be heading home again.

'That's it-on your feet-slowly as she goes- and put your hands behind your back. There's a good lad, do it for old Smithy. Gently does it now, no silly ideas.'

William followed the orders exactly and allowed Sergeant George Smith to tie his hands tightly. The rope bit into his wrists, and his shoulders jarred as the sergeant led him up the dusty side of the dry riverbed in which he had been hiding, out onto the open plain. The old horse snorted and tossed its head against the flies filling its eyes and ears.

'If you're going to get your reward, you're going to have to keep me alive,' said William, weak from the lack of food and water. What little he had managed to bring with him had long run out and he had learned the hard way the truth of the governor's oft-repeated warnings.

'Don't you go trying to tell me my bloody job son. Couldn't give a tinker's cuss if you live or you die, but as I've come all this way...' He directed a thin stream of water from a leather bottle towards his prisoner and William struggled to capture every last drop of the life-saving liquid. 'Waste not, want not,

Will.' His mother's words came flooding back to him, across the years and across the vastness of the oceans that now separated them. He turned his head as the flow finally threatened to drown him and, abject as his situation was, he could not help but see the dark humour of this eventuality: 'drowning'. What a stupid way to die after months refusing to go under.

'Grub later... if you're a good boy. Now, time to get going. At least I know which way I'm heading,' the soldier said as he studied the brass compass around his neck. Get us back in a day, maybe a day and a half , as long as you put one foot in front of the other and don't go dyin' on me. Dobbin here goes at a nice steady pace, clip clop, clip clop, don't you me old son?' He slapped the bony flank before easing himself onto his back and kicking the animal into a plodding, south-easterly, walk.

Thornbush tore at Williams's legs and the summer sun blinded him as he started the long walk back to the camp from which he had made his escape some three days earlier.

'So you didn't get to China then Parker?' the soldier mocked. 'None of them ever does. The sun or snakes get them usually. Then it's the dingoes. Surprised you survived this long to tell the truth.'

In his short time on the run, William had noticed scores of prisoners' bones- their bleached remains picked clean, sometimes surrounded by the remnants of whatever few possessions they happened to be carrying when their spirits finally joined the mass of others in what the natives called 'The Dreamtime'.

'Governor won't be too happy. Ever had a floggin'?'

William said nothing. There was nothing to say. The man was right. No-one ever got away and if you did they brought you back in a box; unless the dogs got to you first in which case there would be no burial and the coffin saved, until the next time...

The following hours were a blur of thirst, flies and scorching sun. William was given sips of water, enough to keep him walking, as a prisoner brought back alive was worth something. A dead one, on the other hand would, indeed, be a criminal waste: a waste of all the hours, days, and months gone into bringing him half way round the world to this land beyond the seas.

The soldier, bored by hours of his own company, made another effort at conversation.

'Can't understand it me'self. You're a good worker. Well-respected, by the gov'nor even. Could make something of yourself. And that admirer of yours- Mary isn't it?- well, you'd have to be properly mad to leave her behind.'

Sometimes William thought that maybe he was going mad. The events of the previous two years had certainly been a madness of sorts. But the pain in his feet and the dryness of his throat told him that not everything was in his mind.

'Don't say much do you Parker? S'ppose you want to forget yer criminal past. Guilt's a terrible burden to bear, so they tell me. Murder wasn't it? Drowned a man in his father's own canal from what I heard! Can see why you weren't too popular!'

'He did drown, but it wasn't me!' William blurted. 'I mean, I was there but he attacked me, and got caught up with something when we fell in the water! He died, but I didn't kill him!' He struggled to contain his emotions as the scene from two years' earlier replayed itself before his eyes. 'I didn't do anything wrong', he added weakly.

The soldier didn't say much for a few seconds. William was young enough to be his son-just- and he could not but help admire his mettle. Could've been a soldier, he thought, if he hadn't been a convict.

'They all say that, don't they Parker-what makes your story different, then?'

William stayed silent and concentrated on placing one weary foot in front of the other. Then he looked up at his captor. 'He was rich. I was poor,' he said, as if this explained everything.

'Who were they going to believe? We dug the canal. He owned it. He attacked me as I lay by the water and whipped me like I was one of his father's horses. We fought and we slipped in. The water was cold and after a while he stopped fighting. Stopped moving even. I went back under but it was no good. He was dead. And so was I.'

'And so, you got sent out here. Fourteen year stretch?'

'That's right. I thought I was going to swing but his servant who saw it happen spoke up and my life was spared. I owe him my life.'

'Quite a story, Parker,' said the soldier, before observing that William was indeed fortunate to still be alive as others amongst them had done no more than steal a rich man's silk handkerchief let alone rob him of his son and heir.

Nothing much more was said until they approached a clump of trees where Sergeant Smith announced they would stop for the night. Within the circle of trees lay a small pool, a billabong, where the horse was allowed to water.

'You can lead an 'orse to water... and in this place you know exactly what he's going to do!' the soldier chortled before indicating where they would sleep that night.

He pointed to a small area of flattened ground in the lee of a sandstone rock the size of the cottage William had grown up in as a child. A circular patch of scorched earth attested to the fact that others had been here before, but the soldier, following a cursory inspection, confirmed that whoever it had been was now long gone, so they should not be expecting a visit that night.

The sky above changed from bright blue through red to the deepest of blacks, the temperature dropping dramatically as the sun disappeared behind the tops of the looming trees. William sat on the hard earth as his captor- his saviour perhaps- readied the camp for the night. A few broken branches, dry and infused with resin, sparked easily into life warding off any wildlife that might be otherwise inclined to investigate the newcomers. Following a simple meal of wild parsnips, dug from the soil and baked in the campfire coals, and as much water as they could drink, both men laid back and stared at the stars. Apart from the occasional crack as a twig exploded into flame, and the far off call of a night animal, it was as peaceful a place as William could recall, the dark beauty unlike anything remembered from his life in England. A billion stars filled the space between the treetops, the darkest of canopies carpeted by the brightest pinpoints of blue-white light.

'Quite a sight, eh, Parker? Almost worth all the trouble you're in.'

William sighed, brought back to earth by the voice from the void. The long walk, the harsh beauty of the surroundings, and now the cosy reassurance of the campfire had led to a relaxation between soldier and convict. As far as was possible between captor and captive the two men liked each other and had even managed to enjoy their brief time together. Smith, William found, possessed a little of the humanity so lacking in others he had had to share his life with over the past two years or more. For his part, Smith liked this lad with his stubborn refusal to be beaten and his genuine wonderment at the world and all that it had to offer: both good and bad.

The soldier described his own life- how he had grown up in a village not unlike William's Hensford home, how he had longed for a world of adventure away from the farms and the hop-fields of Kent, how he had left home at the age of sixteen to join the Royal Marines in nearby Chatham and had found himself, only a few months later, on board HMS Gorgon, part of the Third Fleet bound for the new penal colony in Botany Bay. His own memories of the voyage still fresh, William listened intently to Smith's description of the dire conditions the troops and the thirty or so convicts had to endure as they plied the oceans, first south-west to South America, then east across the southern Atlantic to The Cape, and thence onto New South Wales. The main cargo had been six months' provisions for the nine hundred people now starving in the colony, the ship greeted as a saviour when it arrived on the morning of the spring equinox, September 21st 1791. In December they had watched with a mixture of pride and longing as Gorgon, sails billowing, finally weighed anchor and left Port Jackson for England, taking with her the last of the